Human Physiology

PRENTICE-HALL

FOUNDATIONS OF BIOLOGY PROGRAM
William D. McElroy and Carl P. Swanson, *Editors*

Animal and Plant Diversity
Neal D. Buffaloe

Modern Cell Biology
William D. McElroy and Carl P. Swanson

The Green Plant
Arthur W. Galston

Human Physiology
Robert I. Macey

Investigations of Cells and Organisms
A Laboratory Study in Biology
Peter Abramoff and Robert Thomson

ABOUT THIS PROGRAM

A few years ago the series editors of this biology program were involved in the preparation of a paperback series entitled *Foundations of Modern Biology*. The success of that series led us to explore the possibilities of producing a similar series organized on the basis of a slightly different approach and organization. Extensive inquiry among biology teachers indicated that such a program would fill a real need. With that encouragement, we have planned the present FOUNDATIONS OF BIOLOGY PROGRAM.

Realizing that the subject matter and philosophy of biology are an extremely important part of the liberal education of every citizen, we felt that a biology program should be varied, yet pertinent. It should also do the following: 1. convey something of the meaning, scope, and excitement of biological science as a significant perspective from which to view the world; 2. provide an acquaintance with the world of living things, and of the relationships of one organism to others; 3. provide a knowledge of the structure and function of organisms and of populations; and 4. provide a knowledge of man: his history as an organism, his relation to other organisms, his rise to a position of dominance in the biological world, and the ways in which he functions as an animal and as a human being. In general, these are our goals in the four parts comprising this program.

The FOUNDATIONS OF BIOLOGY PROGRAM also includes a separate volume, *Investigations of Cells and Organisms: A Laboratory Study in Biology* by Dr. Peter Abramoff and Dr. Robert Thomson.

All of us—authors and editors alike—are grateful for the excellent advice and constructive criticism so generously offered by the many teachers who helped in the preparation of this program. Their familiarity with the varied needs of students has been extremely valuable to us. Those who have been particularly helpful, and who deserve our particular thanks, are EDWIN M. FIELDS, CAROL L. CROW, VINCENT J. SILLUZIO, ELIZABETH A. SIMENDINGER, IRWIN SPEAR, and R. W. VAN NORMAN.

—*The Editors*

Human

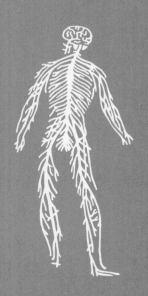

PART 4

FOUNDATIONS OF BIOLOGY PROGRAM

William D. McElroy and Carl P. Swanson, *Editors*

Roy A. Gallant, *Editorial Adviser*

Prentice-Hall, Inc., *Englewood Cliffs, New Jersey*

Physiology

Robert I. Macey

Department of Physiology and Anatomy
University of California, Berkeley, California

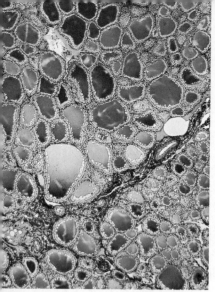

Section: E. Evans
Photograph: A. Blaker

ABOUT THE COVER

Microscopic section through the thyroid gland. This section shows thyroid follicles, which are hollow, spheroid structures with cellular walls. The interior of the follicle is a storage site for the thyroid hormone, which is attached to a protein called thyroglobulin. The interiors of the more active follicles are stained blue, the least active ones red. The stain is Mallory-Azan.

To Ella and Joe

FOUNDATIONS OF BIOLOGY PROGRAM
William D. McElroy and Carl P. Swanson, Editors

HUMAN PHYSIOLOGY
Robert I. Macey

Current printing (last digit):
10 9 8 7 6 5 4 3

Library of Congress Catalog Card Number: 68–10165
Printed in the United States of America

Designer   Merrill Haber

Illustrations   Prepared by Joseph M. Sedacca,
               Robert Bryant, Juan Barberis,
               scientific illustration specialists who are
               also employed as graphic designers at
               The American Museum of Natural History,
               New York, N.Y.

Picture Research   Gabriele Wunderlich

ABOUT THIS BOOK

"The proper study of mankind is man."* We yearn to know who we are and what we are. How did we get here? This book is about the physical bases for our existence. We know that the matter which makes up our body is unstable. When the material parts of our body are separated, they quickly decompose. In this book we will be primarily concerned with the question of how the human body is able to survive some seventy odd years in an environment of both threat and enrichment. Although this is only a small part of what man is, we follow the lead of science which progresses by breaking complex questions into simpler, more manageable ones.

* Alexander Pope, *Essay on Man.*

ROBERT I. MACEY

Berkeley, California

CONTENTS

Human Physiology

1 SURVIVAL AND THE INTERNAL ENVIRONMENT

The face value of the chemical elements of your body is only a few dollars. Yet this few dollars worth of chemicals can lift weights, convert food and air into bones, muscles, and nerves, work mathematical problems and study the very chemicals which make it up. What remarkable transformations have the chemicals undergone to enable them to do these complex and diverse tasks? You, as one of the most recent links in the evolutionary chain going back millions and millions of years, reap the benefits of eons of unceasing biological development.

When you stop to think about the variety of things your body is capable of doing—simple everyday things that we all take for granted—you begin to see what an astounding thing your body really is. For example, what are the processes involved in reach-

Fig. 1.1 Leonardo da Vinci's drawing "The Proportions of the Human Figure after Vitruvius."

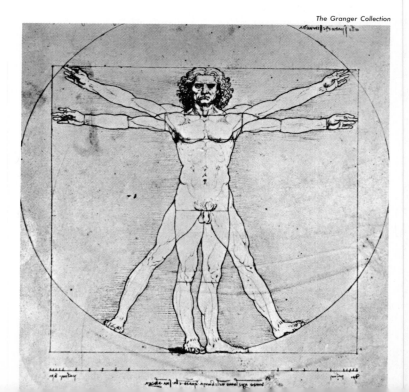

ing out for an object and picking it up? How can you ride a bicycle without concentrating on keeping your balance? When you lift a very heavy weight, why does your heart seem to beat faster? What keeps your heart beating day after day, year after year? When you cut your finger, what chemical processes stop the bleeding?

These are exactly the kinds of questions a **physiologist** is constantly asking, and most of the questions are only partially answered. He wants to know: How does the heart beat? How does a muscle contract? How does a nerve carry messages? And where does the energy come from to perform all of these, and other, tasks? In short, physiologists want to know how living organisms work, yet they find it difficult even to define "living." However, the physiologist knows that the processes he is interested in take place in anything that grows and reproduces itself by undergoing chemical changes. Although human physiology—the subject of this book—is concerned with man's body, many studies of other animals cast some light on the human organism.

The Internal Environment

You have probably always thought that air is the external environment of your body. In a way, of course, it is, yet if you examine a piece of living tissue from your body under a microscope, you will find that its living cells are surrounded by a watery fluid. All of the living parts of your body are inhabitants of water, not air. Those parts that are not moist—the outermost skin, fingernails and hair—are not composed of living cells; they are essentially dead tissue. The fluid medium surrounding cells is called the **extracellular fluid** or, sometimes, the **internal environment.**

Extracellular fluid is about the same in all parts of your body. The fluid surrounding the cells that make up your toes has virtually the same composition as that surrounding the cells of your brain. These fluids have a composition very similar to that of blood plasma, the fluid that circulates in the blood stream. Further, a similar fluid bathes the cells of a variety of different species of animals. Although men, dogs, frogs, lobsters, and crabs are in many ways quite different from one another, the internal environment of each is strikingly similar. The physiologist wants to know why.

Life seems to be possible in these animals only under highly restricted conditions. For one, their cells can stay alive only if they are bathed in an internal environment of specific chemical composition. If the calcium content in a man's blood (normally about 10 milligrams per hundred milliliters of blood) drops to one-half its normal level, he begins to twitch and eventually goes into convulsion, which can be fatal. On the other hand, if the calcium content is increased by one-half, he shows severe depression and is likely to go into a coma, which can also be fatal. There are many other similar examples. Human life, then, is possible only when calcium (and many other substances) are present within certain rigidly fixed proportions. When the proportions are upset, the result can be sickness or death.

Steady State

Knowing that the composition of the internal environment must remain fairly constant, we might now ask how it is kept that way. In the simplest case, we can imagine a container which allows an exchange of materials and energy with the external environment. Sugar, salt, water, and heat enter the container by certain routes and leave it by certain other routes (Fig. 1.2). If sugar enters at exactly the same rate as it leaves, the amount of sugar in the container remains *constant,* despite the fact that it is *continually being renewed.* We would say that sugar is in a **steady state,** meaning that its concentration in the container does not vary, even though it is continually being exchanged with the external environment.

This steady state example corresponds to the internal environment in living systems. For example, certain components in the food we eat are absorbed into the internal environment through the walls of the intestinal tract. They are removed by processes taking place in the kidney, lungs, and skin. Intake and removal are balanced so that the concentrations of many substances (such as salts, sugars, and water) in the internal environment do not change very much.

Although a steady state normally tends to be maintained, the interchange between the internal and external environments varies from time to time. If we move from a warm room to a cold room, the heat exchange between the air and our internal environment alters quite a bit, yet our body temperature remains close to 98.6°F. Again, we may eat an excessive amount of sweets on one day and none at all on the next. The amount of sugar transferred between the external and the internal environments is quite different on the two days, but the concentration of sugar within the blood remains remarkably constant.

Homeostasis and the Steady State

Since the rate of exchange between external and internal environment *does* change from time to time, the

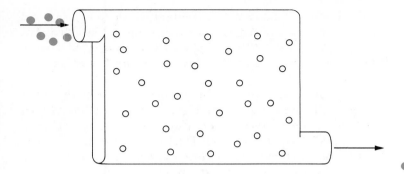

Fig. 1.2 The idea of a steady state is shown in this diagram. During the time six molecules are entering the container, six others are leaving it. The total number of molecules in the container does not change.

body must have some mechanisms for keeping the composition of the internal environment constant. Otherwise, animals could not survive. This tendency to regulate the internal environment, keeping it in a steady state, is called **homeostasis.** The higher we go on the evolutionary tree (moving from simpler to more complex animals), the more vital this process becomes. When homeostasis fails, the central nervous system is often affected first; without homeostasis, the highly developed nervous system and the intelligence of man probably could not have evolved. The many mechanisms involved in regulation—not all of which have yet been discovered—influence the behavior of all the living things we will be studying in this book.

Storage and Feedback as Regulators

Most of us are involved in problems of regulation of one sort or another throughout our lives. For example, say that you want to raise tadpoles in order to observe their stages of development. You need a barrel of rain water, so you put a barrel out in rainy weather, and when it is partly filled you put in some fertilized frog eggs. Rain is pouring into the barrel at the top and draining out through a hole equipped with a valve at the bottom, as shown in Fig. 1.3. To keep the barrel from overflowing and spilling the eggs out, you have to open the drain, yet you want a nearly full barrel at all times. In other words, you want to allow fresh rain to enter, yet want to be able to control the level of the water. The simplest solution is to set the drain valve so that the overflow at the bottom just balances the inflow of rain. But this will work only as long

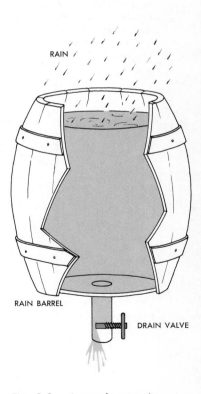

Fig. 1.3 A steady state is maintained because the amount of water running out of the barrel is equal to the amount of rain entering.

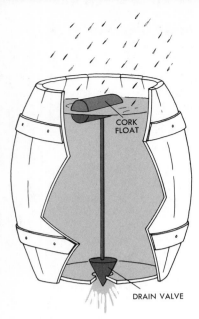

Fig. 1.4 If the amount of rain entering the barrel varies, the automatic drain valve compensates for the change, maintaining a steady state. This is an example of *negative feedback* (Fig. 1.5).

as the rate of rainfall remains constant. Each time there is a change in the rain, you have to readjust the drain valve. The same problem arises in most regulatory systems; you have to devise ways to compensate for *changes* that are not under your control.

How could you concoct a simple device to keep the water level in the barrel constant? As Fig. 1.4 shows, you could float a cork on the water, then attach it to a metal rod with a cone-shaped piece of wood at the end. The length of the rod is exactly equal to the depth of water you want to keep in the rain barrel. When the water is this deep, the piece of wood closes off the drain. If it begins to rain again, the water rises and lifts the cork which, in turn, pulls the wooden plug out of the drain. When the water level and plug sink downward again, the drain opening becomes smaller, and less water flows out. In rainy weather you always have a full barrel of water, but no overflow.

We can represent the response of your system to an increase in rainfall by the diagram in Fig. 1.5.

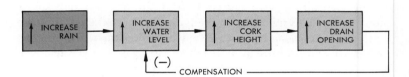

Fig. 1.5

In Figs. 1.5 and 1.7 we use a vertical arrow (↑) to mean *increase,* a descending arrow (↓) for *decrease,* and a horizontal arrow (→) for *leads to.* Figure 1.5 can then be read as:

> An increase in rain leads to an increased water level in the barrel, which leads to an increase in cork height, which leads to an increase in drainage, which compensates for (negates) the increased water level.

The essential feature of the system is that it can be represented as a circle or **closed loop.** Closed-loop systems are called **feedback** systems; information about the response of the system (in this case the water level) is "fed back" to change the response. The feedback in our system is called **negative** feedback because it compensates for, or negates, the increase (change) in water level of the barrel, hence the (−) minus symbol at the end of the feedback loop. Negative feedback tends to *stabilize* a system.

Suppose, as shown in Fig. 1.6, you make a mistake and turn the cone-shaped drain plug the wrong way. When there is a

6

downpour, the water level rises, but this time it closes the drain and the barrel overflows. You have created a vicious circle, which can be represented as shown in Fig. 1.7.

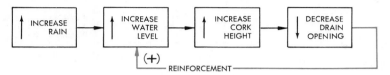

Fig. 1.7

Again we have a feedback loop, but now instead of negating the increase in water level, the feedback reinforces it. We call this a **positive** feedback system, and hence the (+) plus symbol at the end of the feedback loop. In contrast to negative feedback, positive feedback leads to *instability.*

Let us return to the original negative feedback system, the one that kept the water level constant. Although it works fine in rainy weather, you have made no provision for a dry spell, during which the water will evaporate. You need a storage system to supply water if the level is to remain constant.

Figure 1.8 shows one system which fills the need. For dry periods, its response is illustrated in Fig. 1.9. Notice that the

Fig. 1.8 If a storage tank is added to the system, a steady state can be maintained during periods of drought as well as during periods of rain. Rain causes Drain B to open, keeping the water level constant. During drought, water evaporation from the barrel causes Drain A to open, allowing water from the storage tank to enter. At the same time the valve at right closes. (See Figs. 1.9 and 1.10.)

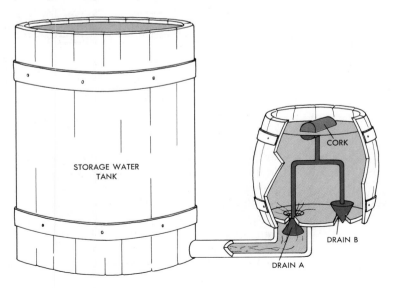

Fig. 1.6 The steady state is abolished if the amount of rain increases, thus raising the cork float and closing the valve. It is also abolished if the amount of rain decreases, thus lowering the float and opening the valve. Both cases are examples of *positive feedback* (Fig. 1.7).

8   *Human Physiology*

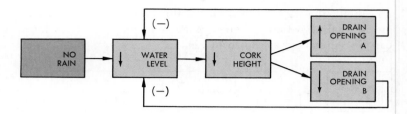

Fig. 1.9

diagram is similar to Fig. 1.5, except that now there is an additional feedback loop for Drain *A*. A decrease in rainfall decreases the water level. As a result, the float falls, lowering Plug *A* into the open position and permitting an inflow of water from the storage tank. At the same time, Plug *B* is dropped into the closed position, preventing water from draining out. The pair of feedback loops (Fig. 1.9) shows how the water level tends to be stabilized during drought.

Figure 1.10 shows what happens in case of heavy rainfall. The water level rises and the float drops. This opens Drain *B*, allowing water to leak out, and closes Drain *A*, cutting off the inflow of water from the storage tank. Again, both loops tend to stabilize the water level.

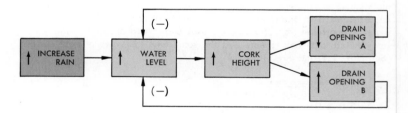

Fig. 1.10

Biological Feedback Systems

Our bodies have countless feedback systems that regulate our internal environment. They frequently make use of storage depots and often use more than one feedback loop. The regulation of plasma calcium is a good example of negative feedback.

Calcium is a common element in many foods. When it enters the intestinal tract it is absorbed into the blood plasma. It leaves the plasma by way of the kidney, which excretes the cal-

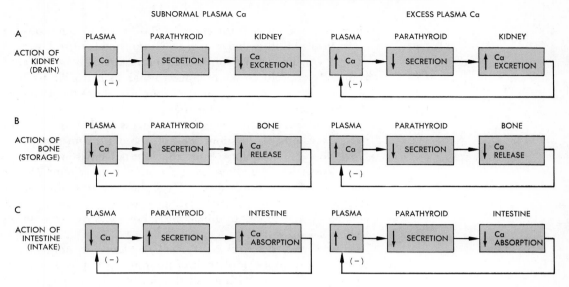

Fig. 1.11 The body tends to maintain itself in a steady state. Here we show how the level of calcium is maintained in a steady state by the parathyroid hormone. The system shown here includes the regulatory actions of drain, storage, and intake, similar to the system shown in Fig. 1.8.

cium in the urine. A steady state of calcium may be obtained by balancing the dietary intake with urinary excretion. However, these two are not the only factors in maintaining the proper concentration of calcium.

Bones form large *storage* depots for calcium, and the plasma can tap these storage supplies in times of need. Regulation of the dietary intake, urinary excretion, and calcium storage is provided by tiny glands located in the neck—the **parathyroid** glands. These glands secrete a substance (a **hormone**) into the blood stream and the blood stream carries the hormone to all organs in the body. Low levels of plasma calcium increase secretion of this hormone. The action of the hormone on the kidney, intestinal tract, and bone provides the three feedback loops illustrated in Fig. 1.11.

Figure 1.11A shows the negative feedback resulting from the action of the parathyroid hormone in regulating the urinary excretion by the kidney. The kidney in this instance is similar to the drain on our water tank. The second loop, shown in Fig. 1.11B, results from the action of the hormone which regulates the transfer of calcium from bone to plasma. In this instance, bone provides an internal storage system, similar to our reservoir tank, which can be tapped when there is too little or no calcium in our diet. The third loop, shown in Fig. 1.11C, results from the action of the hormone which increases calcium absorption from the intestinal tract. The dietary intake of calcium corresponds to rain entering the barrel in our example.

Each of the three loops in the diagram tends to stabilize the plasma calcium level. Notice that the response to low calcium is directly opposite to the response to high calcium. All we have to do to make one diagram in a pair like the other is reverse the direction of the vertical arrows.

To understand other regulatory systems in the body, we ask the same kinds of questions we ask about calcium regulation. How does the substance enter the internal environment, and how does it leave? Is there an internal storage system? How is the level of material sensed? Then, how is this information relayed to something corresponding to the drain valve, or kidney, or storage depot? In other words, how does each step in the feedback loop work?

However, a description of feedback loops is not enough. Ideally, we want a complete description of the entire machinery. In our example of calcium regulation, we would like to know what process the parathyroid gland goes through when it synthesizes and secretes its hormone, and how this activity is governed by calcium. Further, we would like to know how it is possible for the parathyroid hormone to stimulate the kidney to retain calcium, or to stimulate bone to release calcium. Finally, we would like to know why calcium is indispensible. What is its function? How does it act?

The physiologist studies not only the parts of the body in isolation, but also the way various parts work together and keep the animal alive by keeping its internal environment constant. Most of our questions are not fully answered. In this book we will study some of the partial answers discovered by forming and testing theories. These partial answers give us a basis for asking further questions, for forming new hypotheses, and for planning experiments to test new theories.

SUMMARY

Living cells are fragile and very sensitive to changes in their immediate environment. This is especially true of animal cells, which are surrounded by a fluid called the **internal environment.** The sensitive and fragile cells cannot be expected to survive unless the internal environment remains fairly constant.

The gastrointestinal tract, the lungs, the kidneys, and skin are continually involved in the exchange of materials and energy between the internal and the external environments. Nevertheless, the composition of the internal environment is not changed drastically; it is subjected to **regulatory mechanisms** that balance the inflow and outflow of the internal environment, resulting in a **steady state.** The tendency to regulate the internal environment so that it is maintained in a steady state is called **homeostasis.**

Homeostatic regulatory systems can be represented by **feedback loops.** The feedback is *negative* when it compensates for, or negates, any change. Negative feedback tends to stabilize a system. When feedback reinforces a change, we call it *positive* feedback. Positive feedback creates a vicious circle and leads to instability.

FOR THOUGHT AND DISCUSSION

1 What is meant by a **steady state?** What are the **inflows** and **outflows** that could be balanced to maintain the following systems in a steady state: (a) The volume of fluid in a river? (b) The population of a city? (c) The weight of your body? (d) The number of cars on a super highway?

2 Recent experiments suggest that our description of calcium regulation illustrated in Fig. 1.11 is not complete. These discoveries involve a new hormone called **thyrocalcitonin.** Thyrocalcitonin is secreted by the thyroid gland and is believed to decrease the level of circulating blood calcium. If this hormone is important in maintaining a constant level of blood calcium, what do you suppose the effect of calcium might be on the secretion of the thyrocalcitonin by the thyroid gland? Draw a feedback loop.

SELECTED READINGS

Baldwin, E. *An Introduction to Comparative Biochemistry.* New York: Cambridge University Press, 1964.

Cannon, W. B. *The Wisdom of the Body.* New York: W. W. Norton and Co., 1939 (reprinted 1963).

Langley, L. L. *Homeostasis.* New York: Reinhold Publishing Co., 1965.

Rasmussen, H. "The Parathyroid Hormone," *Scientific American* (April 1961) (*Scientific American* reprint #86).

Tustin, A. "Feedback," *Scientific American,* **187** (September 1952), 48.

2 TRANSPORT

Courtesy J. David Robertson, M.D.

Fig. 2.1 A cell membrane is the major barrier to an exchange of materials between cells and their environment. The cell membrane in the above photo is believed to be limited by the two dark stained lines which give it a railroad track appearance.

The exchange of material between the external and the internal environments will be one of the focal points of our study. In addition, we shall be concerned with the exchange of materials between cells and the fluids making up the internal environment (extracellular fluid). All of the substances taking part in these continual exchanges must be transported back and forth in some way. Certain physical forces cause this movement of materials. The most important of these forces arise from *differences* in **pressure, concentration,** and **electrical charge.**

A ball rolling downhill illustrates some important aspects of transport. We would expect that in the diagram below the ball at left rolling down to B would not need to be pushed; but to go

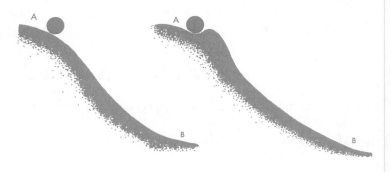

from Point B to Point A, it would have to be pushed all the way. At right the *barrier* would prevent the ball from rolling to Point B, unless it were given a push. Nevertheless, A is still higher than B, so once the barrier is removed the ball will move to B.

At Point A in both situations, the ball has **potential** energy. The force acting on the ball (gravity) pulls the ball from a point where its potential energy is high toward a point where its potential energy is low (*B*). To describe the transport of a ball from *A* to *B*, we must specify two things: 1. the relative heights of *A* and *B*; and 2. the nature of the path. A similar description holds for other types of transport. Although the difference between two given points in a biological transport system may be easy to obtain, the nature of the path may be very difficult to discover.

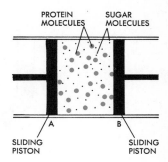

Fig. 2.2 If the pressure on Piston A is greater than the pressure supporting Piston B, there will be a movement of sugar and protein molecules toward the right. This is an example of *bulk flow.*

Pressure Forces and Transport

To show how a difference in pressure causes transport, we could build a device like that shown in Fig. 2.2. We begin by filling a tube with a solution of small sugar molecules and large protein molecules dissolved in water. Then we place one piston at Point *A*, and another at Point *B*. When we push piston *A* harder than *B*, we would expect the fluid to move along the tube to the right. In other words, if the push, or **pressure,** at *A* is greater than the pressure at *B*, the fluid will move in the direction *A* to *B*. The fluid will always move from a region of high pressure to a region of low pressure. Since the entire solution (water, sugar, and protein) flows, we call the movement **bulk flow.**

However, we can stop the flow by changing the nature of the path (Fig. 2.3). If we place a solid wall at *B*, then no matter how hard we push at *A*, there will be no flow. But if we poke holes in the barrier, we will again have a flow from left to right. The extent of the flow will depend on how many holes we poke and how big they are. Like the solid barrier, the porous barrier poses resistance, but only partial resistance—the smaller the holes, the greater the resistance will be, and the more slowly the fluid will move under given pressure. A similar resistance arises in the blood stream when the blood is forced through narrow vessels.

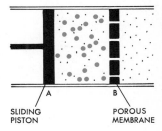

Fig. 2.3 If the stationary barrier at B were a sieve, only the sugar molecules would be permitted to flow through. No matter how great the pressure at A, the protein molecules could not get through. This is an example of *filtration.*

Now, imagine that the barrier at *B* has *very* small holes in it—holes just a little larger than the sugar molecules. The protein molecules are too large to get through. We describe this barrier by saying it is **permeable** to sugar and water, but **impermeable** to protein; that is, sugar and water can penetrate, but protein cannot. When we apply pressure at *A*, only the sugar and water move; the protein stays behind. This process of separating small particles from large particles by pushing them through a sieve-like structure is called **filtration.** We shall see later that filtration is the first step in the formation of urine by the kidney.

We can measure pressure by using a device like the one shown in Fig. 2.4. We place some mercury (Hg) in a U-shaped

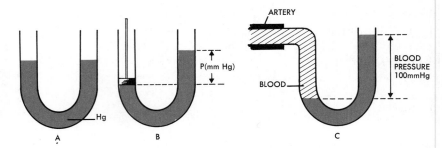

Fig. 2.4   The height of the mercury columns in Tube A is the same because the pressure is the same on each column. In Tube B the heights of the columns are different because of the pressure exerted by the piston. This pressure can be measured by measuring the height indicated by P. In Tube C, the pressure is exerted by the blood and the height of the mercury column gives us a measure of the blood pressure.

tube and let it settle so that the levels in the two limbs of the tube are equal (Fig. 2.4A). Then we place a piston in the left-hand limb of the tube and push down so that the mercury begins to rise in the right-hand limb (Fig. 2.4B). As the mercury rises, its additional weight in the right-hand column exerts a downward pressure. The higher the mercury rises in the tube, the greater the downward pressure becomes. Eventually, the downward pressure exerted by the mercury just balances the force exerted by the piston so that the movement of the mercury stops. The pressure exerted by the piston can be represented by the difference in height between the right-hand column and the left-hand column, as indicated by *P*. This difference is usually measured in millimeters (mm) and, accordingly, we speak of pressure in terms of millimeters of mercury (mm Hg).

The pressure exerted by the heart on the blood in the arteries in a normal human averages about 100 mm Hg. If an artery of an animal were cut and one end of the U-tube were inserted into the artery (Fig. 2.4C), the blood would then push directly on the mercury, just as the piston did in Fig. 2.4B. The difference between the heights of the mercury in the two columns would then give us a direct measure of the animal's blood pressure. When a doctor takes your blood pressure, he does not, of course, cut an artery. However, the indirect (and less precise) method he uses does involve balancing the pressure of your blood against the force exerted by a column of mercury.

In our study of motion caused by differences in pressure, there are two essential factors: 1. the forces which arise from differences in pressure; and 2. the nature of the pathway (for example, the presence of barriers). Similar factors determine the motion resulting from differences in the concentration of liquids separated by a porous barrier.

Concentration Differences and Transport

Whenever there is a difference in concentration of molecules in two regions, there will be a *movement of molecules from the region of high concentration to regions of low concentration.* This movement is called **diffusion.** It results simply from the fact that molecules are in continuous random motion.

For example, suppose that we fill a tank with water and are able to dissolve 18 molecules of sugar into the water on the left-hand side of the tank and 10 molecules on the right-hand side. The broken line in Fig. 2.5 represents a mark on the glass of the tank and visually divides the tank into two halves, Sides *A* and *B*. The sugar is free to move about in the whole tank. Eventually, we count the molecules in each side of the tank again. Now we find that there are 14 sugar molecules in each half. How do we account for this change?

We know that the molecules in the tank are bouncing around completely at random. We repeat the experiment many times, keeping track of all the molecules and averaging the results of our experiments. On the average, half the molecules in Side *A* have been moving to the right, and half have been moving to the left. At the beginning, an average of nine sugar molecules (half of 18) from Side *A* were moving to the right. Of the 10 sugar molecules in Side *B*, five were moving to the left. In other words, while nine sugar molecules were moving across to the right from Side *A*, only five were moving across to the left from Side *B*. Side *A* of the tank had a net *loss* of four molecules, Side *B* a net *gain* of four. Thus, when we take our count at the end of the waiting period, on the average we find the number of molecules equal in both sides of the tank.

Our description of diffusion is based only on the *average* motion of the molecules. This means that our rule (net movement from higher to lower concentrations) may occasionally fail—that is, we must be prepared to find motion that is occasionally different from the average motion. However, 18 molecules was a very small sample. In any tank that we might use, there would be billions upon billions of molecules. Whenever we deal with such huge numbers, significant deviations from average behavior are extremely rare so that our rule about diffusion turns out to be very precise.

Molecules diffuse from a region of high concentration to a region of lower concentration. Eventually the concentrations will be the same in both regions. The time required for the concentrations to equalize depends on how far the molecules have to travel; that is, on the size of the container. Molecules in solution take a long time to diffuse unless the distances are very short.

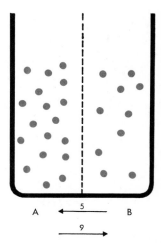

Fig. 2.5 The molecules in this tank (divided by an imaginary line) are more concentrated in Side A than in Side B. In time the concentration will become uniform. Molecules move from regions of higher concentration to regions of lower concentration. This is an example of *diffusion.*

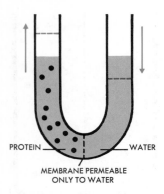

MEMBRANE PERMEABLE
ONLY TO WATER

Fig. 2.6   Water is leaving the region where the concentration of dissolved molecules is low (right-hand column), in favor of the region where the concentration is high (left-hand column). The colored broken lines represent the change in water levels after *osmosis* has taken place. We can stop the motion of the rising water column by applying a back pressure (Fig. 2.7). The magnitude of the back pressure is a measure of the *osmotic pressure.*

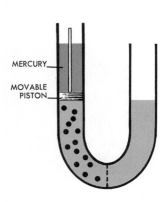

MERCURY

MOVABLE
PISTON

Fig. 2.7

Over a distance of 1 centimeter (cm), diffusion takes about 13 hours before it is nearly complete. Over a distance of 10 cm, the time is about 53 days. Over a distance of only 0.001 cm (10 microns), the diameter of some cells, diffusion is nearly complete in about 0.05 second. If oxygen had to diffuse from the lungs to our feet, it would take years. But oxygen does not travel from the lungs to the body tissues by diffusion. Instead, it is transported by the blood stream (bulk flow). Once the oxygen reaches the tissues, diffusion takes over as the mechanism of transport.

In contrast to bulk flow, which carries everything dissolved in a fluid regardless of concentration, diffusion may transport only one kind of dissolved molecule. In our bodies, for example, salt may be equally distributed throughout a cell, but at a given moment sugar may be more concentrated in one half of the cell than in the other half. In this case, there is a **concentration difference** for sugar, but none for salt. In the absence of a barrier, the sugar diffuses and its concentration becomes equal in all parts of the cell.

If there is a barrier present, such as a cell membrane, the diffusion process is greatly affected by the number and size of the holes in the barrier. The barrier can slow down the diffusion of some molecules and completely prevent other molecules from passing through.

Osmosis

Figure 2.6 shows an example of *water* movement resulting from differences in concentration of dissolved substances (**solutes**). Suppose that we have separated the limbs of a U-tube by a membrane that allows the passage of water but not proteins. The membrane is water permeable, but it is protein impermeable. The left-hand limb has proteins dissolved in it, but the right-hand limb does not. We soon notice that the water in the left-hand column begins to rise as the water in the right-hand column falls. Water is leaving the region where the concentration of *dissolved molecules* is low, in favor of the region where the concentration is high. This process is called **osmosis.** Although we know the conditions under which osmosis takes place, we do not understand its precise mechanisms.

The forces that arise during osmosis can be measured very simply. We insert a piston in the left-hand compartment of a U-tube (Fig. 2.7). Then we apply pressure to the piston by pouring mercury on top of it. The pressure on the piston begins to counteract the pressure of the rising water. If we pour just enough mercury on the piston to exactly balance the force of osmosis, so that the water does not move, we then have a measure of the **osmotic pressure** of the solution on the left. The more molecules dissolved on the left-hand side, the greater will be the osmotic pressure. In a general way, the osmotic pressure may be regarded as the tendency of a solution to draw water to itself. Water will tend to flow from regions of low osmotic pressure to regions of high osmotic pressure.

You can see the effect of osmotic pressure by doing a very simple experiment. Place some animal cells in distilled water and observe the results under a microscope. The cells will begin to stretch and expand until their membranes can no longer contain the contents of the cells. The cause is a difference between the osmotic pressure inside the cells and that outside the cells. There are many molecules dissolved in the fluid inside the cells, so the osmotic pressure there is high and tends to draw water in. But the fluid outside the cell is pure water. Since it is without dissolved substances, its osmotic pressure is zero. Water continues to flow into the cells, stretching their membranes, until they become porous enough to release the contents of the cells.

The results of this simple experiment have obvious applications to experimental work with animal cells. When cells are placed in a solution, we try to make sure that the osmotic pressure of the solution matches the osmotic pressure within the cells. A solution that allows cells to retain their original size is called an **isotonic** solution. A common isotonic solution is isotonic saline. For humans and other mammals isotonic saline is a solution of sodium chloride containing 9 g of sodium chloride per 1000 milliliters (ml) of water.

To study the processes that we have been describing—bulk flow, diffusion, and osmosis—in any specific example, we must know what forces are present and what barriers these forces meet. We must also know whether one force counteracts another. For instance, the pressure on the U-tube shown in Fig. 2.7 counteracted the osmotic pressure of the protein solution, preventing any fluid movement.

Electrical Forces and Transport

Some atoms or molecules carry either a positive or negative electrical charge. Any charged atom or molecule is called an **ion.** Two positively charged ions repel each other, as do two negatively charged ions; however, a positive ion and a negative ion attract each other. The attraction or repulsion of ions in a solution sets up forces in addition to those we have been considering. Salt solutions, in particular, show electrical forces. Sodium (Na^+) and potassium (K^+) ions, for

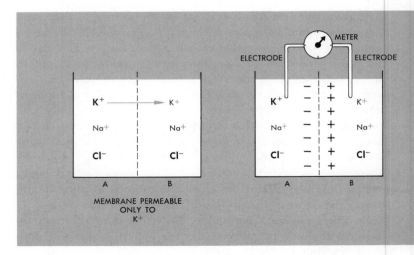

Fig. 2.8   The movement of potassium ions through the membrane upsets the electrical balance. Side *A* is more negative than Side *B*.

example, repel each other in solution because both are positively charged. However, each attracts chloride (Cl^-) ions, which are negatively charged. In a solution, ions are under the influence of pressure, concentration, *and* electrical forces.

The solutions that we ordinarily deal with are electrically neutral. Nevertheless, in some instances, the fact that the solution is made up of charged particles (ions) leads to the development of electrical forces which we cannot ignore. This is particularly true when a solution containing ions must pass through a membrane. The origin of an electrical force across a membrane is shown in Fig. 2.8.

We have a tank partitioned by a membrane. Say that we fill Side *A* with an electrically neutral solution consisting mainly of potassium and chloride ions, plus a small amount of sodium ions. (By electrical "neutrality" we mean that the number of positive charges equals the number of negative charges.) We fill Side *B* with another electrically neutral solution, one consisting mainly of sodium and chloride ions with a small amount of potassium ions. Assume that the membrane allows potassium to pass through, but not sodium or chloride. If we could see the individual ions moving, the first thing we notice is that potassium ions are moving from Side *A* through the membrane to Side *B*. The reason for this movement is that potassium ions are more concentrated on Side *A* than on Side *B*, and they tend to move from an area of high concentration to an area of low concentration.

The movement of potassium ions across the membrane upsets

the electrical balance on both sides of the membrane. Side *A* is now left with more negative than positive charges, and Side *B* is gaining positive charges. As more potassium ions move across the membrane, the excess positive charge accumulating on Side *B* acts as a repelling force. This opposing electrical force becomes larger with each new potassium ion that moves from Side *A* to Side *B*. Finally, the electrical force built up along the membrane is so strong that it counteracts the force of diffusion—no further net transfer of potassium ions can occur.

On Side *A* negative charges have been building up because the electrical effects of chloride ions which have been left behind are no longer compensated for by potassium ions. There is an excess of negative ions on Side *A* and an excess of positive ions on Side *B*. Since negative and positive charges attract each other, these excess ions line up along the membrane. Whenever a membrane separates layers of opposite charges, we say that the membrane is **polarized.**

If we try to measure the amount of K^+ that has crossed the membrane, we find it *so small* that ordinary chemical tests cannot detect it! Yet, even a small number of excess ions produces a significant electrical force. We can measure this electrical force simply by bridging the two sides of the tank with suitable wires (Fig. 2.8). Some electrons (negative charges) making up the metal of the wire are free to move under the influence of electrical forces. When the two ends of the wires, called **electrodes,** are dipped into the solution, one on each side of the membrane, the electrons flow from Side *A* to Side *B*. This flow of electrons (or **current**) can easily be detected with sensitive meters.

Suppose now that we use a membrane permeable to more than one ion, say, to both sodium and potassium, but which is much more permeable to potassium than to sodium. At first, we see the ions lining up just as they did in Fig. 2.8. But gradually a change takes place. Although the potassium ions move very rapidly from Side *A* to Side *B*, occasionally we notice a sodium ion moving from Side *B* to Side *A* (Fig. 2.9). It, too, is moving toward a region of lower concentration (since there are many more sodium ions in Side *B* than in Side *A*) but at a much slower rate. The excess positive charge along the membrane in Side *B* never builds up to the point where it completely stops the diffusion of potassium ions because sodium, also carrying a positive charge, is slowly diffusing through to Side *A*. Each time a sodium ion passes from Side *B* to Side *A*, another potassium ion can pass from Side *A* to Side *B* without affecting the charge distribution across the membrane.

This exchange of Na^+ for K^+ will continue until the concentration differences tend to disappear, and at the end of the

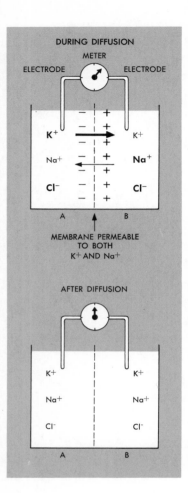

DURING DIFFUSION

METER

ELECTRODE   ELECTRODE

K^+ K^+

Na^+ Na^+

Cl^- Cl^-

A   B

MEMBRANE PERMEABLE
TO BOTH
K^+ AND Na^+

AFTER DIFFUSION

K^+ K^+

Na^+ Na^+

Cl^- Cl^-

A   B

Fig. 2.9 In this case there is an exchange of sodium and potassium ions across the membrane because the membrane is permeable to both. However, the membrane is more permeable to K^+ than to Na^+ and this accounts for the membrane polarization during diffusion. After diffusion is complete (bottom diagram), there is no longer a difference in concentration of K^+ and Na^+. The membrane is no longer polarized.

experiment, we have an equal concentration of both Na^+ and K^+ ions on each side of the membrane. At this time the membrane is no longer polarized. Diffusion caused by the concentration differences has ceased, and the conditions required for polarization of the membrane no longer exist (Fig. 2.9).

Almost every living cell we will be studying has a polarized membrane. Usually the inside of the cell is negative.

Cell Membranes

A living cell membrane is the site of continuous activity; molecules are constantly being transported to and fro across it. This transport is controlled by special properties of the membrane barrier. For one thing, if we surround a cell with both small and large molecules, we notice that only the small ones enter the cell. The large ones seem to be excluded. The cell membrane may have a porous structure with pores so small that they permit only small molecules to squeeze through.

Molecules easily dissolved in oil also penetrate the cell membrane very rapidly. On the other hand, large molecules which do not dissolve in oil are excluded. The cell membrane itself contains an oil-like material called **lipid**. Evidently, molecules which are easily dissolved in oil are also easily dissolved in the lipid structure of the membrane and, therefore, can penetrate the cell. It has been proposed that the lipid is spread over the surface of the cell as a film-like structure, and that the film is supported by a protein network superimposed on both its outer and inner surfaces.

When we begin a more detailed study of cell membranes, we find some things that are puzzling. Some molecules seem to go "uphill," that is, they move through the cell membrane from a region of low concentration to one of high concentration. For instance, the intestinal tract may contain very little glucose (sugar) in its digested foodstuffs, while the bloodstream may have a much higher concentration of glucose. Nevertheless, the cells lining the walls of the intestine can transport the little bit of glucose from the intestine toward the blood.

If we study an individual cell, we find other *apparent* inconsistencies. The inside of the cell, for example, is rich in potassium, and the fluid bathing the outer cell membrane is rich in sodium (Fig. 2.10). The cell membrane is permeable to potassium, but sodium ions permeate much more slowly. We would expect that eventually the potassium and sodium ions would exchange to the point where each is equally concentrated inside and outside the cell. But this does not happen under normal conditions.

However, if we cool the cell (or interfere with the cell's activity in some other way), potassium ions begin to leak out of the cell, and sodium ions begin to leak in. If we wait long enough, the concentrations of both potassium and sodium on both sides of the cell membrane reach equilibrium, just as we would have expected originally.

If we warm the cell to its normal temperature, sodium ions begin moving out of the cell and potassium ions begin moving in. Both are now moving toward the region of high concentration, in other words, "uphill." Eventually, the cell returns to its original state with a high concentration of potassium inside and a high concentration of sodium outside. This cannot be explained by the influence of electrical forces, because both potassium and sodium ions are positively charged, yet they are moving in opposite directions. If one were attracted to a certain region (or repelled from that region) by electrical forces, the other should be also. That is, electrical forces should make them both move in the same direction.

Evidently, cell membranes have the capacity to "pump" solute particles in an "uphill" direction. The exact mechanism of this pumping action is unknown, but energy is required to pump the molecules uphill. The energy is obtained from chemical reactions taking place in the cell (metabolism). Transport which moves in an "uphill" direction is called **active transport.** When we first study a cell, we would expect sodium ions to leak in and potassium ions to leak out. But, apparently as fast as some sodium ions leak into the cell, an equal number of them are extruded by a "pump;" and as fast as potassium ions leak out, an equal number are pumped back in. When we cool the cell, or curb its metabolism by poison, we interfere with the energy supply to the pumping mechanism shutting it down. As a result, the sodium ions which leak in, and the potassium ions which leak out are no longer compensated for by active transport. When we rewarm the cell (or remove the poison), the pumping mechanism begins to operate again, and finally a new steady state is reached. The rate of pumping is just equal to the rate of leakage.

All living cells are capable of active transport in one way or another. Some cells actively transport glucose; some cells actively transport amino acids. Almost all cells transport sodium and potassium ions in the way we have described. Although biologists have built experimental models that transport solutes uphill, and in some ways mimic the actions of cells, the detailed mechanism used by the cells to accomplish uphill transport still remains a mystery.

Fig. 2.10 In a normal cell sodium is pumped out as fast as it leaks in, and potassium is pumped in as fast as it leaks out (top). Cooling the cell depresses the "pump" so that it no longer compensates for the leakage. The cell loses potassium and gains sodium (bottom).

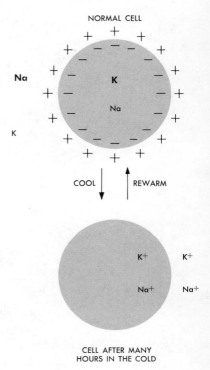

NORMAL CELL

COOL   REWARM

CELL AFTER MANY
HOURS IN THE COLD

The active transport of sodium and potassium ions requires a substantial portion of the cell's total energy and plays an important part in its total economy. For instance, a rich supply of potassium ions within a cell facilitates some chemical reactions involved in protein synthesis, so its accumulation inside the cell may be vital to the life of the cell. Maintaining osmotic equilibrium with the cell's outside environment is also vital. Each cell contains many large solute molecules that cannot be transported out; and because they add to the total osmotic pressure, they tend to draw water into the cell. To counteract this pull, the cell can pump sodium ions out to help equalize the osmotic pressure. Finally, sodium and potassium ions must be present in different concentrations across the membrane of nerve and muscle cells if these cells are to function properly.

SUMMARY

Some of the physical forces involved in movements of molecules arise from differences in **pressure, concentration,** and **electrical potential. Bulk flow** takes place from regions of high pressure toward regions of lower pressure; molecules **diffuse** from regions where they are highly concentrated toward more dilute regions; water flows toward regions where the dissolved molecules are more concentrated **(osmosis).** Positive ions tend to move away from positively charged regions (high electrical potential) toward negatively charged regions (low electrical potential); negative ions tend to flow in the opposite direction. Transport is affected by the presence of barriers. Cell membranes form effective barriers for transport, permitting some molecules to pass through while excluding others.

In many cases, more than one type of force is involved. Osmotic water flow can be prevented, or even reversed, by an oppositely-directed pressure force. The diffusion of ions results in electrical forces that affect the diffusion process. Living cell membranes are able to transport some dissolved substances "uphill," from regions of low concentration to regions of high concentration. The energy required for this **active** ("uphill") **transport** is obtained from chemical reactions taking place within the cell (metabolism). All cells can actively transport potassium ions into the cell and sodium ions out of the cell.

FOR THOUGHT AND DISCUSSION

A membrane separates two solutions of solute S. The solute on the right-hand side is more concentrated than that on the left.

1 If the membrane is permeable to *S*, then immediately after the experiment begins, in what direction will *S* move?
2 If the membrane is permeable to water, but impermeable to *S*, then immediately after the experiment begins, in which direction will the water move?
3 If you wanted to prevent water movement, on which side of the membrane would you apply a pressure (for instance, by pushing on a piston)?
4 Assume that *S* is the salt, sodium chloride (Na^+Cl^-). Further assume that the membrane is permeable to Na^+ but not to Cl^-. Would you expect electrical differences between the two sides of the membrane? Which side would be positive?

SELECTED READINGS

Carlson, A. J., V. Johnson, and H. M. Cavert. *The Machinery of the Body,* 5th Ed. Chicago: University of Chicago Press, 1961.

Hardin, G. *Biology, Its Principles and Implications.* San Francisco: W. H. Freeman and Co., 1961.

Holter, H. "How Things Get into Cells," *Scientific American* (September 1961) (*Scientific American* reprint #96).

Kimball, J. W. *Biology.* Palo Alto, California: Addison-Wesley Publishing Co., Inc., 1966.

Ponder, E. "The Red Blood Cell," *Scientific American* (January 1957).

Weisz, P. B. *The Science of Biology.* New York: McGraw-Hill Book Company, 1963.

3 MOTION: MUSCULAR CONTRACTION

If you touch a live animal it usually responds by moving. Motion is one of the most common signs of animal life. Many cells are capable of some form of movement, but there are certain cells specialized to move various parts of the body, or the whole animal. Breathing movements, heart beat movements, and many, many other forms of motion necessary for homeostasis and survival are caused by the contraction of **muscle cells.**

Types of Muscle

There are three types of muscle: 1. **skeletal** muscle; 2. **cardiac** muscle; and 3. **smooth** muscle. **Skeletal** muscle consists of bundles of muscle cells—long, fibrous cylinders with diameters ranging from 0.01 to 0.1 mm, and a length up to 40 mm. These muscles are under **voluntary** control; that is, we can

Fig. 3.1 This plate illustrates ''the anterior view of the body from which I have cut away the skin, together with the fat and all the sinews, veins, and arteries existing on the surface.'' It displays ''a total view of the scheme of muscles such as only painters and sculptors are wont to consider.'' Andreas Vesalius (1514–1564).

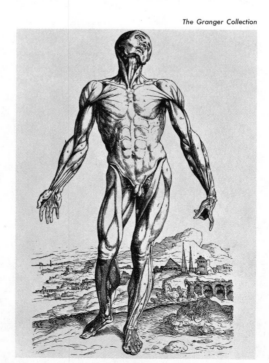

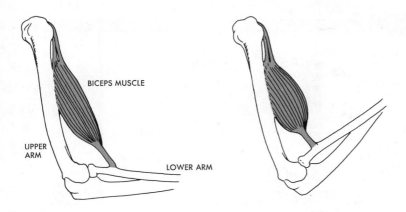

UPPER ARM

BICEPS MUSCLE

LOWER ARM

Fig. 3.2 Contraction of skeletal muscle moves the limbs and other parts of the skeleton. These muscles are under *voluntary* control.

command them to work for us whenever we wish them to. Most skeletal muscles are attached at each end to bones; when the muscles contract, the bones move on their joints. Figure 3.2 shows how contraction of muscles in the upper arm moves the lower arm. In this case, the elbow serves as a pivot. Compared to the other two types of muscle, skeletal muscle is capable of rapid and short bursts of activity. **Cardiac** muscle is the major component of the heart. Its alternating contraction and relaxation is responsible for pumping blood. **Smooth** muscle is found imbedded in the walls of hollow internal organs, for example, in the intestinal tract, in the bladder, and in blood vessels. In contrast to the other two types, smooth muscle is most often involved in slow, sustained contractions. Cardiac and smooth muscle are not under voluntary control.

Muscle Contraction

There are two classifications of muscle contraction—**isotonic** contraction, and **isometric** contraction. An isotonic contraction involves actual shortening of the whole muscle. When you pick up a weight, your limbs move. It is the shortening of muscle which is responsible for the motion of the limbs. On the other hand, you may try to pick up a weight which is too heavy, say, something that weighs 300 pounds. In this case there is no motion. Nevertheless, your muscles become tense; they pull on the weight but not enough to move it. When muscles exert a pull or tension but do not move, we say that they have undergone **isometric contraction.**

How can we imagine a muscle exerting tension, but not shortening? One possibility is shown in Fig. 3.4. Gross muscle is composed of many different parts, but not all of the parts shorten or change dimension when a muscle contracts. Those

Fig. 3.3 A microscopic view shows that skeletal muscle is made of long, fibrous cells which contain many nuclei. Note the stripes running perpendicular to the surface. (See p. 28.)

William Windle, M.D.

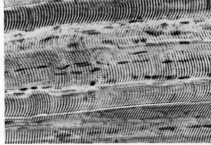

Fig. 3.4 This diagram shows the relationship between the *series elasticity* and *contractile element* when a skeletal muscle is relaxed, and in isometric contraction.

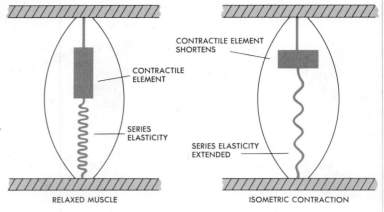

CONTRACTILE ELEMENT

CONTRACTILE ELEMENT SHORTENS

SERIES ELASTICITY

SERIES ELASTICITY EXTENDED

RELAXED MUSCLE   ISOMETRIC CONTRACTION

parts that do are called **contractile machinery.** The contractile machinery must be attached to other parts of the muscle, called the **series elasticity.** The series elasticity has the properties of a stiff rubber band. When we stretch the series elasticity, it exerts some tension, but it in itself does not *cause* the fundamental change in dimension. In the second part of Fig. 3.4, the contractile machinery shortens and stretches the series elasticity, thus creating tension. In an isometric contraction some shortening may actually occur in the contractile machinery, but all the shortening goes into stretching the series elastic component. As a result, there is no gross movement, only a certain amount of tension develops.

The most interesting part of muscle is the contractile machinery. The physiologist wants to know the structure of this machinery, and its immediate source of energy. We now think that the contractile machinery is composed largely of two proteins, **actin** and **myosin.** The immediate source of energy for contraction seems to be a very highly reactive compound called **ATP (adenosine triphosphate).** This compound contains 3 phosphate groups, as illustrated in Fig. 3.5. It is a product of the cell's

Fig. 3.5 When phosphate is split off from ATP, energy is released. This energy can be used by the cell to do work.

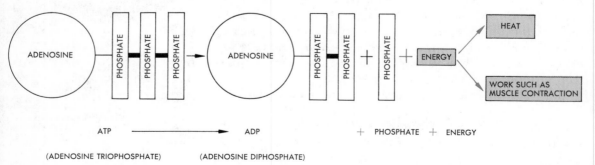

ADENOSINE | PHOSPHATE | PHOSPHATE | PHOSPHATE → ADENOSINE | PHOSPHATE | PHOSPHATE + PHOSPHATE + ENERGY

HEAT

WORK SUCH AS MUSCLE CONTRACTION

ATP ⟶ ADP + PHOSPHATE + ENERGY

(ADENOSINE TRIOPHOSPHATE)   (ADENOSINE DIPHOSPHATE)

metabolism and is formed, for example, when glucose (blood sugar) is broken down to carbon dioxide and water. A sizable fraction of the energy released by the breakdown of glucose is stored in small packets in the form of ATP molecules. This energy, in turn, can be released when phosphate groups are split off from the ATP, as shown in Fig. 3.5. Among the many chemical reactions which liberate energy, the splitting of ATP plays a unique role—energy liberated by the splitting off of phosphate groups can be used by the cellular machinery to do work.

What evidence allows us to make these statements? First of all, muscle does contain large amounts of actin and myosin. Secondly, by acting as a **catalyst,** myosin speeds up the breakdown of ATP to ADP. More evidence comes from a study of muscle fibers which have been soaked in a solution of glycerol for several days. This treatment leaches out most of the soluble constituents of muscle, including salts, sugar, and ATP. The framework which is left behind consists primarily of actin and myosin. This framework is called a **glycerinated** muscle fiber. If now we wash off a glycerinated muscle fiber and add ATP to it, it will contract and lift the same weights that an intact muscle will. Furthermore, we can show that during the process of contraction ATP is split to ADP. These glycerinated fibers may be kept in a deep freeze for several months without losing their capacity to respond to ATP.

An intact muscle not only contracts, but it also relaxes. When ATP is added to a glycerinated muscle, the muscle fiber contracts, but does not relax. This poses a new problem—how does relaxation take place? Recent experiments have shown that addition of juices from a minced, fresh muscle to a contracted glycerinated muscle causes the contracted muscle to relax. Apparently, the intact muscle has some **relaxation factor** which keeps the muscle in a relaxed state until it is excited. Further experiments have shown that the relaxation factor contains essential components, tiny fragments that are parts of a muscle cell structure called **sarcoplasmic reticulum,** which bind calcium ions. Now free calcium ions are needed for the reaction of glycerinated muscle with ATP to take place. The effect of the relaxing factor, then, may be simply the result of its binding with calcium. If this is so, then during contractions somehow or other the calcium must be released from these fragments; just how this takes place is not known.

Structure of the Contractile Machinery

In the past 10 years, we have learned a great deal about the structure of intact skeletal muscle, how actin and

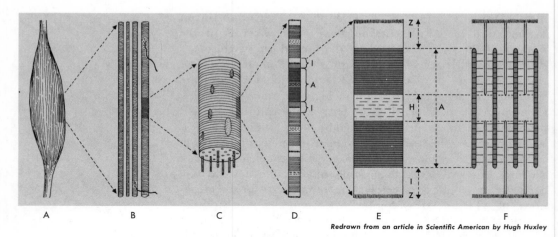

A   B   C   D   E   F

Redrawn from an article in Scientific American by Hugh Huxley

Fig. 3.6 Schematic drawing of skeletal muscle as it is dissected and seen under higher and higher powers of magnification. A represents a whole muscle (similar to Fig. 3.2). B represents muscle fibers (similar to Fig. 3.3). C shows the fibrils that run through a single fiber, while D and E show details of the striped fibril (similar to Fig. 3.7). The overlapping relation between the actin and myosin filaments is shown at F.

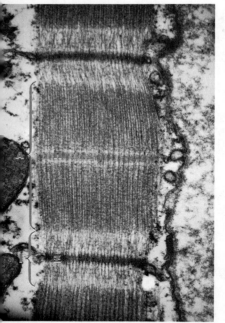

Courtesy J.G. Forte

Fig. 3.7 This electronmicrograph (enlarged 24,000 times) shows some of the structure of muscle fibrils. The A bands, the I bands and the Z lines are very prominent. Compare this figure with Fig. 3.6D and E.

myosin are arranged, and how they move during contraction. The series of illustrations in Fig. 3.6 shows the details of muscle structure as they are brought out by observing muscle under greater and greater magnification. Part A of the diagram represents muscle as we see it with the unaided eye. Whole muscle is composed of a great number of fibers or cells. Each fiber is about 100 microns (0.1 mm) in diameter. If we look at the single cells shown in Part B, we see that each cell has stripes. Further magnification of a single muscle cell (Part C) shows that the cell also has very fine fiber-like structures running lengthwise throughout the muscle. These very fine structures are called **fibrils.** The fibrils are about one micron thick. They are striped, and their stripes are aligned in such a way that they give the cells a striped appearance. Details of the stripes are shown in Parts D and E, representing a single fibril. The wide, dark striped portion is called the **A band,** and the light portions between the A bands are called the **I bands.** Frequently, a light region is seen in the middle of the A band; it is called the **H zone.**

The fibrils seem to make up the contractile machinery. In between the fibrils are many of the usual chemical constituents found in most types of cells. In addition, structures that seem to be part or all of the relaxing factor structure can be found in these spaces.

When we examine a fibril under an electron microscope, we see even smaller fiber structures. They are called **filaments.** These filaments are 50 or 100 angstroms (0.005 to 0.01 micron) thick. Their arrangement is shown in Part F of Fig. 3.6. The A bands in the fibril seem to be made of relatively thick filaments which overlap with thinner filaments. Bridges can be seen reaching out from the thick filaments toward the thin filaments. Toward the middle region of the thick filaments there is no overlap with the thin filaments, and it is in this region that the H zone appears.

By placing muscle in special salt solutions, we can dissolve the myosin without destroying the actin. Whenever this is done, the thick filaments disappear. In other words, we identify the thick filaments with myosin. However, it is also possible to dissolve out the actin. Whenever this is done, the thin filaments disappear; for this reason we identify the thin filaments with actin.

Our current ideas are that when muscle contracts, or when muscle stretches, the myosin components and the actin components do not crumple or stretch out, but remain fixed in their lengths. What does happen is that the filaments slide over each other, with the result that the ends of the actin filaments come closer together (contraction). Parts A, B, and C of Fig. 3.8 show muscle in the stretched, relaxed, and contracted states according to this idea. If the idea is correct, then we would expect that in an intact muscle the length of the A bands does not change whenever the muscle is contracted or stretched. This is, in fact, found to be the case. Further, we would expect that the length of the I bands would decrease when the muscle contracts, and increase when it stretches. This also is found to be so. Finally, the H zone begins to disappear as the muscle contracts, and increases in length during stretching. This is just what we would predict on the basis of this sliding filament hypothesis.

Since the small bridges seen in the electron micrographs provide the only contact between the thick and thin filaments, we now think that the actual work of contraction and the use of energy take place in these elements. Somehow or other, these small bridges are supposed to make contact with the thin filaments and propel them toward one another during contraction. Although we have traced the mystery of contraction to these small bridges, we have yet to learn the details of their actions.

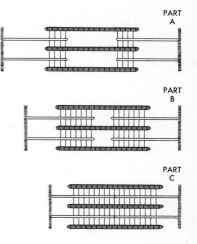

PART A

PART B

PART C

Fig. 3.8 This diagram shows the relationship between the actin and myosin filaments of skeletal muscle in the stretched (A), relaxed (B), and contracted (C) states.

SUMMARY

Most body movements are caused by the contraction of muscle. There are three types of muscle: **Skeletal** muscle (responsible for moving the bones of the skeleton) is frequently involved in rapid, short bursts of activity. **Cardiac** muscle (responsible for the pumping of blood by the heart) contracts and relaxes with each beat of the heart. **Smooth** muscle (found in the walls of hollow internal organs and blood vessels) is often involved in slow, sustained contractions. Skeletal muscle is under **voluntary** control. Smooth and cardiac muscle are not.

Muscle contraction can be classified into two different types. In an **isotonic contraction** the muscle shortens. In an **isometeric contraction** the muscle does not shorten but becomes tense.

When the contractile machinery is examined under the electron microscope, it appears to be made up of two types of filaments. The thinner filaments are made of protein called **actin.** The thicker filaments are made of the protein **myosin.** The actin and myosin filaments overlap one another. When the muscle contracts, these filaments slide upon each other and the extent of overlapping increases. When the muscle is stretched, the extent of overlapping decreases. The interaction between the actin and myosin filaments is believed to occur through regularly spaced bridges that can be seen extending from the thick filaments toward the thin ones. The energy for contraction is made available when a phosphate is split off from **ATP.** Intact muscle appears to contain a "relaxation factor," which keeps the muscle in a relaxed state until it is excited. The relaxation factor is probably a part of the muscle structure able to bind calcium ions.

FOR THOUGHT AND DISCUSSION

1 When you pick up a weight, your muscles undergo both isometric and isotonic contractions. Which comes first? Explain.

2 The two ends of a muscle are tied to a rigid support so that the muscle cannot change its length. The muscle is then stimulated. How could you tell the difference between this muscle and another similar muscle that was not being stimulated? (What tests would you perform?)

3 Suppose that you examine two muscles of the same size and weight and find that one muscle can lift heavier weights than the other. Can you suggest any possible differences (in the muscles) that could account for this difference in their ability to do work?

4 The amount of force that can be exerted by a muscle during contraction and the amount of energy that the muscle uses depend (among other things) on the length of the muscle. For example, if the muscle is stretched enough and then stimulated, it does not exert any force. From your knowledge of

the fine structure of muscle, and of what happens during stretching, can you suggest a reason why stretching a muscle beyond a certain length prevents it from exerting any additional force when it is stimulated?

SELECTED READINGS

Asimov, I. *The Human Body, its Structure and Operation.* Boston: Houghton Mifflin Co., 1963.

Hardin, G. *Biology, its Principles and Implications,* 2nd Ed. San Francisco: W. H. Freeman and Co., 1966.

Hayashi, T. "How Cells Move," *Scientific American* (September 1961) (*Scientific American* reprint #97).

Huxley, H. E. "The Mechanism of Muscular Contraction," *Scientific American* (December 1965) (*Scientific American* reprint #1026).

Huxley, H. E. "The Contraction of Muscle," *Scientific American* (November 1958) (*Scientific American* reprint #19).

Satir, P. "Cilia," *Scientific American* (February 1961) (*Scientific American* reprint #79).

Stumpf, P. K. "ATP," *Scientific American.* (April 1953) (*Scientific American* reprint #41).

Winton, F. R. and L. E. Bayliss. *Human Physiology,* 5th Ed. Boston: Little, Brown, and Co., 1962.

4 INFORMATION TRANSFER: NERVES

The cork float in our water tank in Chapter 1 was useful because it responded to the change in the water level; however, this response alone was not enough. Somehow or other, the float had to be in communication with the valve regulating the outflow. The communication linkage was provided by a rod. In our other example of feedback and control in regulating systems, the parathyroid gland responded to the level of calcium in the blood. It communicated with the gastro-intestinal tract, the kidney, and bone by secreting a chemical into the blood stream. Once the chemical arrived at these organs, the action we described took place. In this chapter we are going to take a close look at ways in which information is transferred from one part of the body to the other. In general, there are two ways: 1. through the secretion of **hormones;** and 2. through "messages" carried by **nerves.**

The Role of Hormones

Any chemical that is released by one organ and affects another organ can be regarded as a **hormone.** It acts as a chemical messenger that coordinates the activities of different organs. Usually a hormone is carried from one organ to another by the blood stream.

The method of hormonal communication is illustrated in Fig. 4.1. The gland releases hormone into the blood stream, and the blood stream carries the hormone to all organs in the body. Even though all organs receive the hormone, they are not all influenced by it. The parathyroid hormone, for example, affects the kidney, the intestinal tract, and bone, but has little effect on other organs, such as the heart and lungs.

THE NERVOUS SYSTEM

Figure 4.2 shows the nervous system of man. The three major components are the **brain, spinal cord,** and

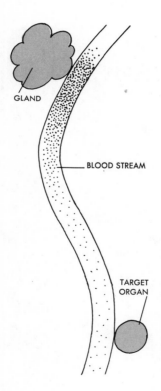

GLAND

BLOOD STREAM

TARGET ORGAN

Fig. 4.1 In general, there are two ways in which information is transferred from one part of the body to another. One way is through the action of hormones, which are "chemical messengers."

1 BRAIN

2 SPINAL CORD

3 SYMPATHETIC GANGLIA

4 VAGUS NERVES (PARASYMPATHETIC)

5 SPINAL NERVES

6 VERTEBRA

7 SPINAL CORD

8 SENSORY NERVES
(CARRY IMPULSES TO THE CNS)

9 MOTOR NERVES
(CARRY IMPULSES FROM THE CNS)

10 SPINAL NERVES
(MIXED, SENSORY AND MOTOR NERVES)

THE NERVOUS SYSTEM

Fig. 4.2 Another way information is transferred from one part of the body to another is through the action of nerve impulses. The large illustration shows three key parts of the nervous system: the brain, spinal cord, and the nerves that link these structures to the rest of the body. The chains of sympathetic ganglia are shown in solid red, parasympathetic nerves in black, and spinal nerves gray.

The inset shows a cross section of the spinal cord as it lies incased in the vertebral column. The central gray area is heavily populated with nerve cell bodies. The lighter area surrounding the central gray is made up of nerve axons running to and from the brain.

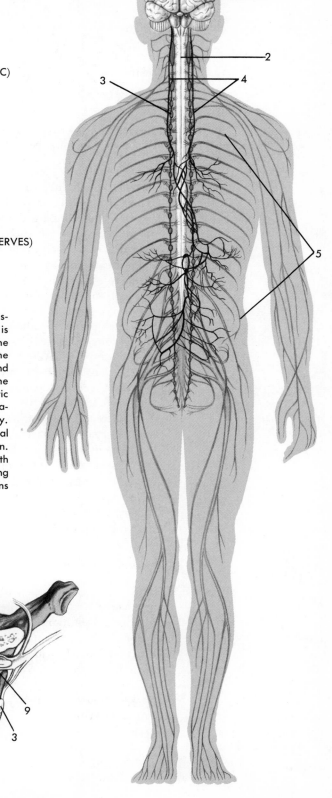

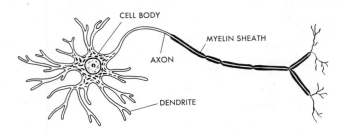

Fig. 4.3   A nerve cell consists of a cell body, dendrites, and a single long axon. Axons may be up to a meter long.

nerves, which link these two structures to other parts of the body. Nerves linking the brain with the body are called **cranial** nerves. Those linking the spinal cord with the body are called **spinal** nerves. If we sliced any one of these nerves we would find that it is made up of cylinders of very fine structure. These cylindrical structures are called **axons.** They are actually portions of nerve cells (Fig. 4.3). Nerve cells are called **neurons** and, like any cell, they have a nucleus and a cell membrane. In addition, they may have several very short structures called **dendrites,** which extend from the cell in virtually every direction. The single long fiber, the axon, is specialized to carry messages. Frequently, it is covered with a thick fatty sheath called **myelin,** which gives the characteristic white color to nerve fibers. The nerves in your body are cable-like structures, each containing a great many axons.

The combination of brain and spinal cord is called the **central nervous system** (abbreviated **CNS**). The CNS coordinates many of the body's activities. Some nerve axons carry messages from the surface and interior of the body to the CNS. These axons are called **sensory fibers.** Other axons carry messages from the CNS to muscles and glands. These axons are called **motor fibers.** Messages carried by motor fibers can be considered as commands that regulate the activity of muscles and glands.

Nature of a Message

Suppose that you were able to remove a nerve and the muscle it is attached to. You place the nerve and muscle in a special solution, called **Ringer's Solution,** whose salt composition resembles that of the internal environment. If you now give the nerve an electric shock (or heat it, hit it, or pinch it), the muscle will shorten. When you stimulate, or excite, the nerve, information of some sort, which we will call a nerve **impulse,** travels along the axon to the muscle, resulting in a muscle response. What, exactly, is this "impulse" that travels along the nerve fiber?

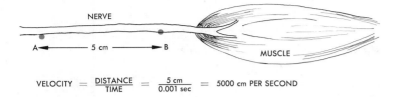

Fig. 4.4 This diagram shows one method of measuring the velocity of nerve impulse. (See text for details.)

We can study the properties of a nerve impulse by setting up in a laboratory the nerve muscle preparation just described. For simplicity, assume that we have a single axon connected to the muscle. We can now measure how fast the nerve impulse travels by the simple arrangement shown in Fig. 4.4. Suppose that we stimulate the axon at Point *A* and measure the time it takes for the muscle to respond. Next, we stimulate the axon at Point *B*, five centimeters closer to the muscle. We find that it takes less time for the muscle to respond when Point *B* is stimulated. Evidently, the difference in the time required for the muscle to respond in these two experiments must be due to the time required for the impulse to pass along the axon from the Point *A* to *B*.

In a typical experiment, if *A* and *B* are five centimeters apart, the muscle responds $\frac{1}{1000}$ second sooner when we stimulate *B* than when we stimulate *A*. In other words, it takes the nerve impulse $\frac{1}{1000}$ second to travel five centimeters. In one second the impulse would have traveled 5000 cm, so the velocity of the nerve impulse is 5000 cm per second (50 meters per second, or about 110 miles per hour). When we study other axons, we find that the velocity may vary, but it will almost always fall somewhere between one and 100 meters per second. In general, axons with large diameters conduct impulses faster than axons with small diameters.

In this type of experiment, we stimulate the nerve axon and use the response of the muscle simply to indicate whether or not the impulse has traveled along the axon. Occasionally we find it difficult to tell whether we are really studying the axon or the muscle. It would be very useful if we could find in the axon itself some change taking place during activity that serves not only as an indicator of the nerve impulse, but that also gives us information about the nature of the impulse. We do have some clues.

When a nerve-muscle preparation is stimulated, many changes occur in the axon just before the muscle contracts. For example, a small amount of heat is produced, there is a very

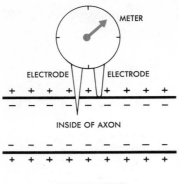

MEMBRANE AT REST

Fig. 4.5 When at rest, the membrane of a nerve axon is electrically polarized, with the inside of the axon negative in relation to the outside.

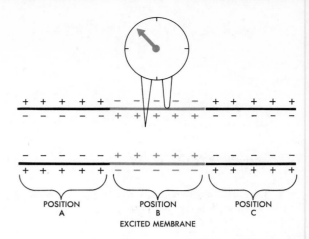

EXCITED MEMBRANE

Fig. 4.6 When a nerve impulse moves along the axon, it is accompanied by a wave of reversed polarity (colored area). The inside of the axon at the excited site of the membrane is positive in relation to the outside.

small volume change, and there are electrical changes. The electrical changes are most striking and are easily measured.

Figures 4.5 and 4.6 show how electrical changes may be measured along the axon. We embed an electrode in the axon and connect it through some measuring meter to an electrode resting along the outside of the membrane. The first measurement shows that the axon membrane is polarized when at rest; the inside is negative with respect to the outside. Now we stimulate the axon. Since we know the speed of the nerve impulse, we can estimate where it will be at each moment following stimulation. When the impulse passes the recording electrodes at Position *B*, the polarity is reversed; in this part of the axon the inside is positive with respect to the outside (Fig. 4.6). If we move the electrodes to Points *A* or *C*, the result is the same when the impulse passes these points.

As the impulse moves along the axon, the polarity is reversed. In other words, the passage of a nerve impulse down an axon is accompanied by a wave of reversed polarity. This wave of reversed polarity traveling down the nerve fiber is called the **action potential.** Whenever we stimulate the axon of a nerve-muscle preparation and find the muscle responding, we also find the action potential traveling along the axon. Further, the action potential travels at a speed exactly equal to the speed of the nerve impulse mentioned earlier. All of the properties of the nerve impulse that we can measure by using the nerve-muscle preparation are shared by the action potential. The action potential seems to be a clear sign of the passage of the nerve impulse, and frequently we tend to think of the two as a single event.

What happens to the action potential when we change the strength of the stimulus? We find that weak stimuli do not pro-

36

duce any response (action potential) in the axon. As we increase the strength of the stimulus, there is still no response until we reach a certain level called the **threshold.** Stimuli whose strength lie above the threshold all produce the same action potential. In a way, the same thing happens with a stick of dynamite. If you gradually raise the temperature of a stick of dynamite by heating it, the dynamite eventually explodes, but increasing the temperature beyond this point (the threshold) does not increase the intensity of the explosion. You either get the explosion or you don't. Similarly, in a nerve fiber we get an action potential or we do not. For this reason, we say that the nerve fiber behaves in an **all-or-none** way. The size of the action potential is the same, no matter how large the stimulus might become.

After being stimulated, a nerve fiber can recover and carry an impulse over and over again. If two stimuli are given to a nerve fiber a few seconds apart, each stimulus produces a nerve impulse. If, however, the second stimulus is given within about $\frac{1}{1000}$ of a second after the first stimulus, only one impulse occurs. Recovery from the first stimulus requires a very short, but measurable time. This short recovery time is called the **refractory period.** The existence of a refractory period of about $\frac{1}{1000}$ of a second means that there is a maximum of about 1000 impulses per second that can be carried along a nerve fiber.

A *threshold* stimulus intensity, an *all-or-none response,* and a *refractory period* are three of the most striking properties of nerve axons. In recent times, physiologists have been able to describe these and other properties in terms of ion transport across the axon membrane.

Polarization of Nerve Membranes

The inside of a nerve cell, like all cells, is rich in potassium and poor in sodium. As you saw in Chapter 2, the active transport process located in the membrane pumps sodium ions out and potassium ions into the cell. The fluids outside the cell, however, are rich in sodium and poor in potassium ions. Considering the concentration forces across the cell membrane, we see that potassium ions are in position to diffuse out of the cell, while sodium ions are in position to move inward. What happens depends on the permeability of the membrane to potassium and sodium ions.

When resting, a nerve membrane is much more permeable to potassium. As a result, small amounts of potassium ions tend to diffuse outward, leaving the cell and building up positive charge on the outside. The resting membrane is polarized—the outside is positive and the inside is negative.

Fig. 4.7 The polarity is reversed at the excited site of an axon because the excited part of the membrane is more permeable to sodium than to potassium.

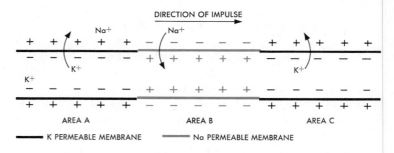

During the passage of an impulse, however, the membrane polarity reverses. The inside is now more positive than the outside. This happens because the membrane suddenly becomes more permeable to sodium than to potassium, and sodium enters the cell faster than potassium leaves. In Fig. 4.7, Areas *A* and *C* of the membrane are inactive, while Area *B* is active. In this figure, the impulse (Area *B*) is traveling from left to right. Fractions of a second ago it was at Area *A*, but *A* has recovered and is a resting cell membrane—negative on the inside, positive on the outside. Compare Area *A* with Area *B* (where the impulse is at this moment). Then compare it with Area *C* (where the impulse will be a fraction of a second from now).

The size of the action potential is limited by the concentrations of sodium and potassium ions on the two sides of the cell membrane. Normally these concentrations do not vary to any appreciable extent. As a result, every time the nerve is excited, the action potential is of the same size. In other words, it behaves in an **all-or-none** way.

Whenever a nerve is stimulated, the effect of the stimulus is to make the cell membrane more permeable to sodium than to potassium. It is this property of a nerve membrane that distinguishes it from ordinary membranes. Although we know that it happens, we do not yet know *how* a nerve cell membrane changes its permeability in response to a stimulus. However, we do know that for a stimulus to be effective, it must in one way or another begin to *weaken* (*decrease*) *the polarity of the membrane*. Then the membrane responds by increasing its sodium permeability. Once the sodium permeability has increased, sodium ions rush in and the membrane polarity will be reversed. The reversed polarity of an excited membrane lasts for less than $\frac{1}{1000}$ of a second. Apparently, the highly sodium-permeable state cannot persist. Potassium ions once again leak out much faster than sodium ions enter, and the membrane soon returns to its normal condition. During rest the tiny amount of sodium ions that have leaked into the cell are pumped out by the active transport mechanism, and the tiny amount of potassium ions that have leaked out are pumped back in.

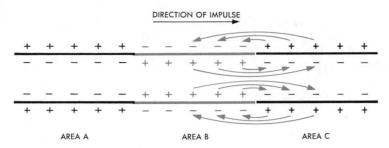

AREA A   AREA B   AREA C

Fig. 4.8 The excited part of an axon membrane (Area *B*) affects adjacent Area C by decreasing its polarity. The decrease in polarity stimulates Area C. The impulse "moves" to Area C and thus travels along the axon.

A question we now must ask is how does an impulse *travel* along an axon? As shown in Fig. 4.8, Area *B* is the active portion of the nerve cell membrane, being positive on the inside and negative on the outside. As the impulse moves along to the right, the polarity of the membrane is reversed. Now exactly what happens to the membrane's inside and outside charge at Area *C* as a result of the reversed polarity that now exists at *B*? On the outside of the membrane, the positive charge at *C* is attracted to and moves toward *B*. On the inside, the positive charge at *B* is attracted to and moves toward *C*. The net result at *C* is that the positive charge is taken away from the outside of the membrane; at the same time, positive charge is added to the inside of the membrane. In other words, the polarity at *C* has been weakened, *just as though we had stimulated it!* The membrane at *C* responds to this slight loss of polarity by increasing its sodium permeability. As a result, positively charged sodium ions enter the cell and the polarity at *C* becomes reversed, that is, Area *C* is excited.

Notice that the conditions for change in membrane polarity at *C* also occur at Area *A*. In other words, the active area at *B* can excite adjacent areas in *both* directions. If we excite a nerve in the middle of the fiber, we indeed find that the impulse spreads in both directions. In the body, however, axons are never stimulated in their middle regions; they are always excited at one end, so that the impulse travels in only one direction.

We see from the discussion above that "messages" are carried from one part of the body to another in a form called nerve impulses. Since each axon responds in an all-or-none way, all of its impulses are identical. If each impulse is no different from any other impulse, then by itself an impulse cannot convey much information. We must, then, look for *patterns* of impulses in order to detect different types of information.

This situation is like the Morse code. For the most part, single dots and dashes do not mean much by themselves; however, certain patterns of dots and dashes indicate letters that can form words. The code used by the nervous system depends on both the *number of nerve impulses* arriving at a given place during each unit of time, and on the *specific axons* that carry the impulses. Somehow, the brain is able to interpret these patterns and to convey its commands to muscles and glands by a similar code.

Sensory Receptors

Impulses sent toward the CNS normally originate in structures called **sensory receptors,** which are distributed throughout the body. These receptors are especially sensitive to particular types of stimuli. For example, the eye is sensitive to light, the ear to mechanical vibrations, or sounds, and the tongue to chemical stimuli, or taste. Other examples of receptors are those which are sensitive to touch, or to heat, or to cold, or to pressure, or pain.

These receptors are always associated with a sensory nerve axon. Sometimes the receptor simply consists of free nerve endings, as in the case of axons that enable us to feel pain. Other times the axons are embedded in an elaborate structure which makes the receptor sensitive to a specific kind of stimulus. An example of this would be the ear. In all cases, however, stimulating the receptor results in the same type of response: action potentials are set up on the sensory nerve axons and carried to the CNS. But remember, as far as we can tell, the impulses are the *same* in all sensory axons, whether they come from the ear, or the eye, or from pain receptors in the toe.

Although the stimulus for the eye is light, the messages, or impulses, which are perceived by the brain reach the brain in total darkness. Messages of cold are carried along nerves which are just as warm as any body structure. Even though all the messages are simple action potentials, you still know whether you have been stimulated by light or by cold.

Apparently, the messages that reach your brain can be interpreted primarily on the basis of where the nerve axon carrying the impulse is located. Thus, you may shine a flashlight in your eye and "see" light, or you may get hit in the eye and see flashes of light. When you are hit, the blow might be strong enough to stimulate the deeply embedded sensory nerve axons leading from the eye to the brain. All the brain "knows" is that impulses were on sensory nerve axons coming from the eye, so it interprets the impulses as light, and you "see stars." If a person's arm has been amputated, he may complain of pain in the arm that is no longer there. The stump of the arm still contains the severed nerves which originally led from the amputated arm to the brain. These severed nerve ends may be highly irritable.

When impulses are sent along these nerves the brain responds as it always has and interprets the messages as signaling pain from the arm that is no longer there.

The brain not only has to interpret *where* the message comes from, so that it can assign the proper sensation to it, but it must also be able to tell how *intense* the stimulus is. It does this in two ways: 1. As the stimulus intensity grows larger and larger, the frequency at which the sensory axons send out impulses becomes greater. 2. The intensity of the stimulus will determine how many axons are made active. The more intense the stimulus, the more axons will be sending in impulses. Thus, the type of information that is fed into the brain is simply what axons are "firing" and how fast they are firing. It is on the basis of this simple type of coding system that the brain must act.

Motor Nerves

A similar code conveys "command" information from the CNS to muscles along motor nerves. If we stimulated a single nerve axon attached to a muscle, we would find a single action potential followed by a very brief contraction lasting less than $\frac{1}{10}$ of a second. This very brief contraction and subsequent relaxation which follows a single stimulus is called a **twitch.** With a possible exception of blinking of an eyelid, we normally do not see twitches in a healthy person. Most muscle contractions last much longer and result in smooth, sustained motions. This is because the motion of a muscle in a healthy person is generally not the result of a single nerve impulse going toward it. Instead it is the result of a whole train of impulses, one following the other in rapid succession.

The first impulse in such a train reaches the muscle and causes the muscle to contract, but before the muscle has time to relax, a second impulse arrives; and before the muscle can relax from the second impulse, a third impulse arrives. In this way a rapid succession of impulses keeps a muscle contracted. Smooth and sustained muscle contractions result from the super-position of many simple twitches and are called **tetanizing** contractions. The CNS can increase the size of contraction in two ways: 1. by increasing the number of axons carrying impulses, so that more muscle fibers are activated; and 2. by increasing the frequency of impulses, so that each contracting muscle fiber is more effective.

Nerve axons are not the only tissues that carry action potentials and that can be excited by electric shock. If you apply a threshold electrical shock directly to the surface of a muscle

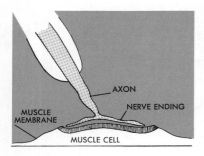

Fig. 4.9 At the neuromuscular junction there is a tiny but distinct gap. When a nerve impulse reaches the end of an axon, the axon releases a chemical transmitter that diffuses across the gap and excites the muscle.

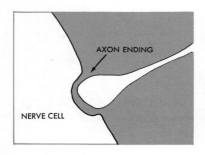

Fig. 4.10 There is also a tiny but distinct gap at the synaptic junction. When a nerve impulse reaches the end of an axon, the axon releases a chemical transmitter that crosses the gap and stimulates or inhibits the neighboring nerve cell.

cell, it will result in an action potential that travels over the entire surface. This is invariably followed by a contraction. The steps leading from an action potential on the muscle surface to contraction of the muscle are not known. However, the properties of the action potential on the surface of a muscle cell or nerve axon do not seem to differ very much.

Passage of Action Potentials Between Cells

When a muscle is excited by nerve impulses, action potentials travel along the nerve fiber to the junction between nerve and muscle (*neuromuscular* junction). Arrival of the impulse excites the muscle fiber so that an action potential spreads over the muscle surface, resulting in contraction of the fiber. The transmission of an impulse from nerve to muscle is called **neuromuscular transmission.**

Impulses are also transmitted from neuron to neuron. For example, the axon of a sensory neuron enters the central nervous system and connects to the dendrites or cell bodies of other neurons. They in turn connect to still others. The junction between the ending of a neuron and a cell body (or dendrite) is called the **synapse,** and transmission of the impulse at this point is called **synaptic transmission.** A nerve cell of the CNS receives many synaptic endings on its dendrites and cell body—sometimes thousands of them. This means that each neuron receives information from many other neurons. The endings look similar, like little buttons pressed on the surface membrane. Actually, a small space separates the axon ending from the surface membrane of the next neuron.

The junction between cells plays an important role in the transmission of excitation. One special property of these junctions is that *conduction takes place only in one direction.* When a muscle is excited directly by an electrical shock, an action potential spreads over the surface of the muscle but does not go backward up the nerve fiber. On the other hand, the action potential does spread down the nerve fiber to the junction and from the junction to the muscle. In synaptic transmission, the action potential always goes from the axon to the cell body of the next neuron, never in the reverse direction.

Another special property of these junctions is that the junctional region itself seems subject to fatigue or subject to the action of certain drugs. For example, a drug called **curare** (which was used by the Indians to poison their arrows) prevents the passage of an impulse from a nerve to the muscle. When the junction is poisoned with this drug, stimulation of the nerve does not make the muscle contract. Yet, in spite of the drug, the nerve carries action potentials; and if the muscle itself is stimulated directly, it contracts. This means that the nerve is intact and that the muscle is intact. Both are capable of carrying an impulse, but somehow or other the impulse does not pass across the junction.

In Figs. 4.9 and 4.10 you can see that at both the neuromuscular and synaptic junctions, there is a tiny, but distinct gap between the ending of the axon and the muscle or nerve cell. Many years ago it was thought that nerve endings release a chemical and that this chemical some how bridged the gap between the nerve ending and the adjacent cell. At first the idea seemed far-fetched, but in 1921, Otto Loewi showed that it was not at all far-fetched when he performed an ingenious experiment on heart muscle.

Loewi knew that stimulation of the **vagus** nerve slowed the heart's beat. His problem was to show that a chemical was released when the vagus nerve was stimulated, but he was not certain of which chemical he was looking for. He used two frog hearts, one with an intact vagus nerve, the other without. The first heart with the intact vagus nerve was arranged so that fluid bathing it could be collected. When he stimulated the vagus nerve of the first heart, it began to beat at a slower rate. This was expected. However, if he now placed the fluid from the first heart into the second heart, the beat of the second heart also slowed—even though he did not stimulate any nerve leading to the second heart. The only contact between the two hearts was the fluid. Some chemical released by stimulating the vagus nerve of the first heart accumulated in its bathing fluid. When this fluid was applied to the second heart, the second heart behaved exactly as if its own vagus nerve had been stimulated (Fig. 4.11).

Sometime after Loewi had performed the experiment, he identified the chemical as **acetylcholine.** Afterwards, an enzyme which destroys the acetylcholine was found. This was called **cholinesterase.**

Each impulse traveling along the vagus nerve releases a small amount of acetylcholine. The acetylcholine diffuses from the nerve ending to the adjacent heart muscle and slows the heart. This action does not last very long because cholinesterase found in the junctional regions soon destroys the acetylcholine. The effect of a single impulse is terminated very rapidly and the junctional tissue is returned to its normal state, ready for the arrival of more impulses.

Experiments have also shown that acetylcholine is an **excitatory** transmitter for nerve impulses arriving at skeletal muscle junctions. Eash time an impulse arrives at the junction, a small

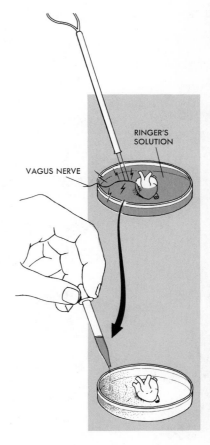

Fig. 4.11 Stimulation of the vagus nerve releases a chemical transmitter (acetylcholine), which slows the heart. We can recover some of the transmitter and transfer it to a second heart. The second heart slows just as if its own vagus nerve had been stimulated.

amount of acetylcholine is released and diffuses across the gap between the nerve and the muscle. Once across the gap, the acetylcholine increases the permeability of the muscle membrane to ions. This results in a depolarization capable of stimulating those parts of the muscle membrane near the neuromuscular junction. Again, this action does not last very long. Cholinesterase located in the junctional region quickly destroys the acetylcholine. The rapid release and subsequent rapid removal of acetylcholine is required if the characteristics of an impulse are to be maintained in crossing the junction.

Inhibition

In Loewi's experiments, we saw an example where stimulation of a nerve decreases, or **inhibits,** a response. Stimulation of the vagus nerve caused the heart to slow down. Stimulation of some nerves leading to smooth muscle causes the muscle to relax rather than to contract. This is another example of inhibitory action of nerves.

We find a very important example of inhibition by nerve axons in synaptic transmission. Figure 4.12 shows how we might study it. Suppose that Nerve Axon 1 and Nerve Axon 2 both lead to the cell body of Nerve Axon 3. Nerve Axon 1 is an ordinary excitatory axon. As Part A shows, when we stimulate Nerve Axon 1 impulses are transmitted out along Axon 3. If we stimulate Axon 2 (Part B), nothing happens. With no other information, we might conclude that Axon 2 has no effect. However, if we stimulate Axon 1 and Axon 2 at the same time (Part

Fig. 4.12 This diagram shows how the inhibition of synaptic transmission might be demonstrated. Axon 1 is an excitatory fiber. Axon 2 is an inhibitory fiber. If both fibers are stimulated at the same time (Part C), Axon 2 inhibits the excitatory effect of Axon 1.

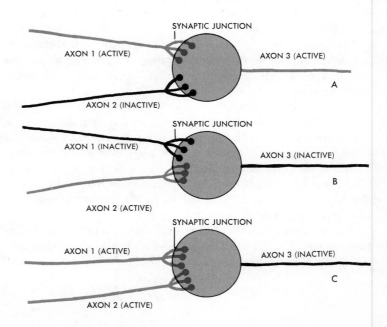

C), we still get no response. The action of Axon 2 somehow prevented, or inhibited, the excitatory action of Axon 1. In this case, we say that Axon 2 is an **inhibitory** fiber.

We now think that inhibition is caused by some inhibitory chemical that is released at the nerve ending. In contrast to excitatory chemicals that depolarize the structure which they excite, inhibitory chemicals do the reverse. They *increase* the polarization of the structure. This increased polarization raises the threshold. Although we know the chemical substance involved in neuromuscular transmission, we have yet to identify the chemicals involved in most cases of synaptic transmission.

Reflex Actions

The simplest coordinated movements that you make—blinking, sneezing, or suddenly withdrawing your hand from a hot stove—seem to be automatic reactions that are brought about almost immediately when there are certain changes in the environment. You withdraw your hand from a hot stove even before you know that you have been burned. These involuntary reactions involve nerve impulses and are called **reflexes.**

In all reflexes, the transfer of information follows a pathway known as the **reflex arc.** As Fig. 4.13 shows, a reflex arc has five components: 1. a **receptor,** which is excited by a stimulus and starts a nerve impulse on its way; 2. a **sensory nerve,** which carries the impulse to the CNS; 3. the **CNS,** where the sensory nerve may branch and make many synaptic connections with other neurons; 4. a **motor nerve,** which carries the impulse to the muscle or gland; 5. the **effector,** which is the muscle or gland activated by the impulse.

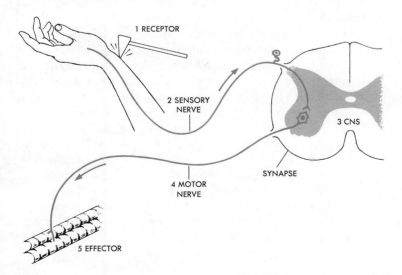

Fig. 4.13 This diagram shows the components of a simple reflex arc that has a synapse in the spinal cord.

Autonomic Nervous System

Many reflexes that help control the internal environment involve a special part of the nervous system called the **autonomic nervous system (ANS).** This system consists of nerves making up the motor pathway to the heart, stomach, intestine, and other internal organs. These nerves are not under voluntary control; that is, you cannot make your heart beat faster on command. The nerve axons of the autonomic nervous system leave the spinal cord and brain and are mixed with other nerve axons in the cranial and spinal nerves. They differ from other nerves that go directly to skeletal muscle. Autonomic nerves, unlike motor nerves which go directly to the skeletal muscles they control, first make synaptic connections with other neurons which relay impulses to the organs (Fig. 4.14).

The two major divisions of the autonomic nervous system are called the **sympathetic** and **parasympathetic** nervous systems. Sympathetic nerves leave the middle regions of the spinal cord. Parasympathetic nerves leave the central nervous system from the upper regions where they travel in cranial nerves, and from the lowermost regions of the spinal cord where they travel in spinal nerves. Most internal organs of your body are supplied with both parasympathetic and sympathetic nerve fibers.

In general, these two types of nerves work in opposite ways. For example, impulses traveling along the sympathetic nerve fibers toward the heart increase your heart beat rate, whereas impulses traveling along the parasympathetic nerves leading to the heart decrease its rate. When impulses traveling along the autonomic nerve fibers reach the end of the line—the contact point with some organ—they exert their action by releasing a chemical transmitter. Parasympathetic nerve fibers release acetylcholine. Sympathetic nerve fibers release a transmitter called **noradrenalin.**

Some of the nerve fibers of the sympathetic nervous system do not follow the general rule of ending at a relay station. Instead, they go directly to the **adrenal** gland. There they release acetylcholine which stimulates the adrenal gland, causing it to secrete a mixture of adrenalin and noradrenalin. This mixture is then carried by the blood stream to all parts of the body and acts on various organs. Thus, adrenalin and noradrenalin are hormones. Adrenalin and noradrenalin have very similar actions. Noradrenalin, remember, is the transmitter of the sympathetic nervous system. So the secretion of the adrenal glands produces the same physiological effects as massive stimulation of the sympathetic nervous system. The heart beat becomes stronger when the sympathetic nerves are stimulated because noradrenalin

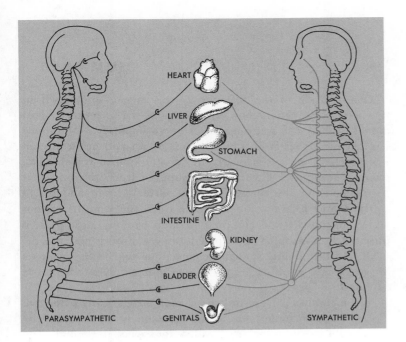

HEART

LIVER

STOMACH

INTESTINE

KIDNEY

BLADDER

GENITALS

PARASYMPATHETIC

SYMPATHETIC

is released at the sympathetic nerve endings. The same thing happens when the adrenal gland secretes hormones, at which time noradrenalin and adrenalin are carried to the heart by the blood stream. In both cases, the heart is responding to the same or almost the same substances.

When we examine the effects of sympathetic stimulation of various organs, a pattern begins to emerge. We find that sympathetic stimulation causes a number of events: 1. widening of air passages leading to the lungs; 2. constriction or narrowing of blood vessels in the skin and in the intestinal tract, resulting in blood being shifted from the digestive organs and skin to the muscles; 3. a general slowing down of movements in the intestinal tract; 4. an increase in the force and rate of heart beat; 5. release of the blood sugar from the liver. All of these activities prepare the animal for emergencies: such as running or fighting. The widening of the air passages makes it easier for the animal to breathe faster and get more oxygen. Blood is shifted from regions where it will not be needed during the emergency (the intestinal tract, for example) to skeletal and heart muscle which will need oxygen and blood sugar. The heart beats faster and stronger so that blood circulates through the muscles at a greater rate. Blood sugar is released from storage in the liver into the blood stream where it will be available to supply muscles with energy.

In the chapters that follow we shall see many examples of the influence of the autonomic nervous system in the control of the internal environment of an animal.

Fig. 4.15 The *sympathetic nervous system* readies the animal for action.

Courtesy Black Star

47

SUMMARY

Coordination of the activities of the various organs within the body is brought about principally by the secretion of **hormones** and by the transmission of **nerve impulses.** A hormone is a chemical that is liberated by one organ and has a physiological effect on another organ. Nerve impulses travel along **axons. Sensory** nerve axons carry impulses from different parts of the body to the **central nervous system** (brain and spinal cord). **Motor** axons carry impulses from the central nervous system to muscles and glands. In a simple **reflex,** an impulse is initiated in a **receptor** and carried along a sensory nerve to the CNS. At this point, **synaptic** connections with other neurons are made and impulses are sent along motor nerves to a muscle or gland.

The membrane of a resting nerve axon is electrically **polarized.** The passage of an impulse along the axon is accompanied by a wave of reversed polarity called the **action potential.** The electrical properties of nerve fibers have been described in terms of the movements of sodium and potassium across the axon membrane.

Nerve impulses behave in an **all-or-none** way and are practically identical. A single impulse cannot convey much information. The brain and body rely on *patterns* of impulses (the number of impulses arriving during each second at a given place) to provide meaningful information.

Action potentials pass between different cells at the **neuromuscular** and **synaptic junctions.** When the action potential arrives at the junction, a **chemical transmitter** is released. It diffuses across the junction and acts on the adjacent muscle or nerve cell. Some transmitters have an **excitatory** effect; others **inhibit.**

The motor pathway to the internal organs is known as the **autonomic nervous system.** This pathway is not under voluntary control. It is divided into two systems: the *sympathetic* and *parasympathetic* nervous systems. Most organs are supplied by both sympathetic and parasympathetic nerves. The actions of the sympathetic and parasympathetic nerves are usually antagonistic. In general, synpathetic nerve impulses help prepare the animal for emergencies.

FOR THOUGHT AND DISCUSSION

1 Acetylcholine and noradrenaline are sometimes called *neuro hormones.* Why is this name appropriate?

2 If parasympathetic nerves leading to the intestine are stimulated, the contractile activity of the intestinal muscle is increased. If the vagus nerve to an isolated heart is stimulated and fluid bathing the heart is removed and placed on a strip of intestinal muscle, the contractile activity of the intestinal strip is also increased. Why?

3 If calcium is removed from the fluid bathing a nerve or muscle, the nerve (or muscle) becomes very irritable and may become excited, even in the absence of any stimulus. If the parathyroid glands are removed from an animal, it very often begins to twitch. Can you relate these two findings? (Recall the discussion of the parathyroid gland in Chapter 1.)

4 If sodium is removed from the fluid bathing a nerve fiber, what would you expect to happen to the action potential?

5 Compare the excitation and conduction of a nerve impulse with the ignition and transmission of a spark along a fuse. In what ways are they similar? In what ways do they differ?

6 When a nerve impulse travels down a nerve axon, that portion of the axon lying immediately behind the action potential is in its refractory period. How does this help to ensure one-way conduction of the nerve impulse?

SELECTED READINGS

Carlson, A. J., V. Johnson, and H. M. Cavert. *The Machinery of the Body,* 5th Ed. Chicago: University of Chicago Press, 1961.

Eccles, J. C. "The Synapse," *Scientific American* (January 1965) (*Scientific American* reprint #1001).

Katz, B. "The Nerve Impulse," *Scientific American* (November 1952) (*Scientific American* reprint #20).

———. "How Cells Communicate," *Scientific American* (September 1961) (*Scientific American* reprint #98).

Keynes, R. "The Nerve Impulse and the Squid," *Scientific American* (December 1958) (*Scientific American* reprint #58).

Loewenstein, W. R. "Biological Transducers," *Scientific American* (August 1960) (*Scientific American* reprint #70).

Loewi, O. "On the Humoral Transmission of Heart Nerves," in *Great Experiments in Biology,* ed. by M. L. Gabriel and S. Fogel. Englewood Cliffs, N.J.: Prentice-Hall, Inc., 1955.

Winton, F. R. and L. E. Bayliss. *Human Physiology,* 5th Ed. Boston: Little, Brown, and Co., 1962.

5 CIRCULATION

Unlike simpler animals, complex animals have certain groupings of cells that become specialized in their ability to perform certain tasks. These "communities" of cells are called **organs.** The lungs, for example, are organs that exchange oxygen and carbon dioxide with the external environment; and the intestinal tract processes food so that it can be used by the cells of the body. In order for a system of organs to function in harmony, the material products of each organ must be available to all cells of the body. The brain, for example, is completely dependent on the lungs for its oxygen supply. If the brain is deprived of oxygen for more than a few minutes, the brain cells begin to

Fig. 5.1 Transport of various materials between different parts of the body is essential to the organism. Transport is performed by circulation of the blood, here visible in the blood vessels in the human mesentery.

William Windle, M.D.

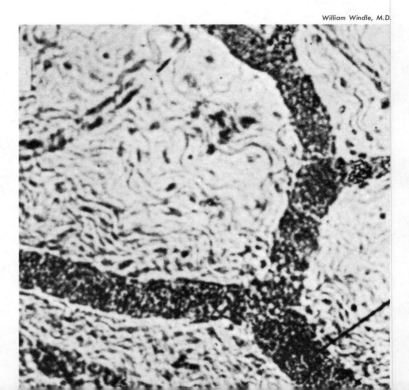

degenerate. Transport of various materials between different parts of the body, then, is essential. The task of transport from organ to organ is performed by circulation of the blood.

The circulatory system consists of a complex network of tubes, or blood vessels. Each of the trillions of cells in the body is close to at least one of these vessels. Blood circulates continuously, picking up products from one organ and delivering them to others. In a way, we can think of the circulatory system as "stirring" the internal environment so that its composition does not differ greatly from one place to another in the body.

The circulatory system has several features enabling it to perform these tasks effectively. One is a pumping system to keep the blood moving. This job is performed by the heart. Second, there must be some means for materials carried by the blood to reach the cells, and for materials in the cells to reach the blood. This exchange takes place in minute blood vessels called **capillaries.** Third, the circulatory system is able to adjust itself to the changing needs of the body. During exercise, muscles have a greater need for oxygen and blood sugar; this need is met by increasing the blood supply to the muscles.

Heart Muscle

The continuous flow of blood is brought about by the rhythmic contraction and relaxation of heart muscles. The heart is a hollow cavity with muscular walls. A thick partition divides the heart cavity into a right and left half. When the muscular walls relax, both the right and left half fill with blood. When the heart beats, the muscles contract; blood is squeezed into vessels called **arteries,** which direct the blood away from the heart toward the organs of the body (Fig. 5.2).

Like any muscle, the heart can be stimulated, and it will conduct action potentials. In many ways, it behaves like a skeletal muscle, but there are some exceptions. Skeletal muscles contract only if they receive some external stimulus. Ordinarily, the stimulus is a nerve impulse leading to the muscle. This is not true of heart muscle, which seems to be capable of exciting itself. Even if we cut all of the nerves leading to the heart, it will continue to beat. This capacity of self-excitation is common to all heart tissue.

If we remove the heart of a cold blooded animal (a frog, say), place it in a dish and cover it with Ringer's Solution, the heart continues to beat—even when it is completely disconnected from the body. If we now cut the heart into pieces, even the pieces continue to beat. However, some pieces beat faster than others. Those from the upper parts of the heart (the **atrium**) beat faster than those from further down (the **ventricle**).

Fig. 5.2 The motion of blood through the body is continuous. It travels in a circular path and is driven by rhythmic contraction and relaxation of the heart.

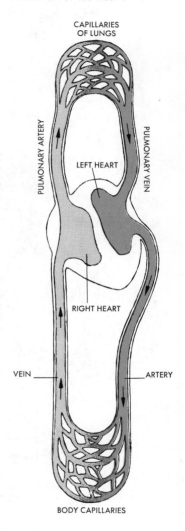

CAPILLARIES OF LUNGS

PULMONARY ARTERY

PULMONARY VEIN

LEFT HEART

RIGHT HEART

VEIN

ARTERY

BODY CAPILLARIES

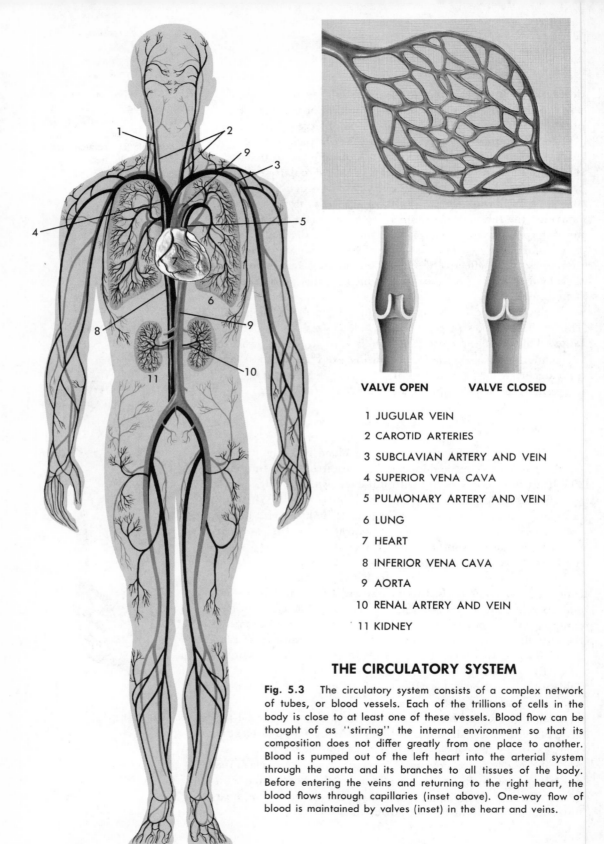

VALVE OPEN   **VALVE CLOSED**

1 JUGULAR VEIN

2 CAROTID ARTERIES

3 SUBCLAVIAN ARTERY AND VEIN

4 SUPERIOR VENA CAVA

5 PULMONARY ARTERY AND VEIN

6 LUNG

7 HEART

8 INFERIOR VENA CAVA

9 AORTA

10 RENAL ARTERY AND VEIN

11 KIDNEY

THE CIRCULATORY SYSTEM

Fig. 5.3 The circulatory system consists of a complex network of tubes, or blood vessels. Each of the trillions of cells in the body is close to at least one of these vessels. Blood flow can be thought of as "stirring" the internal environment so that its composition does not differ greatly from one place to another. Blood is pumped out of the left heart into the arterial system through the aorta and its branches to all tissues of the body. Before entering the veins and returning to the right heart, the blood flows through capillaries (inset above). One-way flow of blood is maintained by valves (inset) in the heart and veins.

We do not know what causes this built-in rhythm of the heart. In a normal heart, the various parts do not beat at different times and with independent rhythms. This is because there is an excellent conduction system in the heart. The first piece of tissue that becomes excited generates an action potential. The action potential is then quickly transmitted to all parts of the heart, exciting the entire tissue. As a result, the entire heart beat is coordinated, pumping with maximum force and sending the blood surging into the arteries.

The Pathway of Blood Flow

Blood leaving the left half of the heart enters a single artery, the **aorta** (Fig. 5.3). The aorta branches like a tree into smaller and smaller arteries. Each of the smaller arteries carries blood to the different tissues of the body. Within the tissues, the smallest arteries empty into a network of even smaller tubes—the **capillaries.**

Capillaries can be seen only with the aid of a microscope. They have very thin porous walls which are easily penetrated by small molecules like sugars, oxygen, carbon dioxide, salts, and amino acids. These molecules simply diffuse through the capillary walls and enter the fluids surrounding the cells. Oxygen, for example, is consumed so rapidly by the cells that the concentration of oxygen in the cells is low compared with the concentration of oxygen in arterial blood. As a result, oxygen diffuses from the capillary vessels to the cells.

After passing through the capillaries, blood enters the **veins.** Small veins merge into larger veins which carry the blood back to the right side of the heart (Figs. 5.2 and 5.3). From here the blood is pumped by the right side of the heart into the pulmonary artery which carries the blood to the lungs. In the lung capillaries the blood recharges with oxygen and rids itself of excess carbon dioxide. It then collects in the pulmonary vein and is carried back to the left side of the heart.

Figure 5.4 shows the heart in more detail. In addition to being divided into a right and left side, each side is subdivided into two chambers—the atrium and the ventricle. At rest the atrium serves as a storage depot for blood returning from the veins toward the heart. When the heart begins its beat the atruim contracts first. Although it may help fill the ventricles with blood, it plays a very minor role in the pumping of blood. A moment later the ventricles contract sending the blood into the arteries. The ventricles contribute most of the pumping action of the heart. The right ventricle is responsible for pumping blood through the lungs; the left ventricle is responsible for pumping blood through the rest of the body.

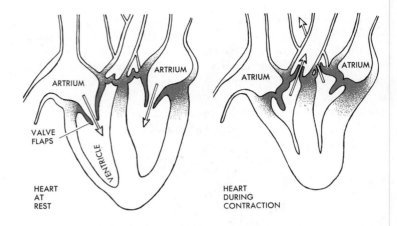

Fig. 5.4 Blood flows into the heart from the veins when the heart is at rest. When the heart contracts, blood is forced into the arteries. Valves in the heart prevent blood from flowing in the reverse direction.

Drawn after Carlson, Johnson, and Cavert

HEART AT REST

HEART DURING CONTRACTION

ARTRIUM ARTRIUM ATRIUM ATRIUM

VALVE FLAPS

VENTRICLE

Fig. 5.5 Total artificial hearts, like the one shown here, are still in the early experimental stage.

Photograph by Harold Friedman, work by Dr. Adrian Kantrowitz

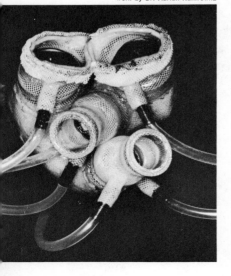

One-Way Flow

When the heart muscles contract, why isn't blood squirted backward into the veins as well as forward into the arteries? And when the heart relaxes, why doesn't blood flow into it from the veins and arteries?

Imagine that the heart is transparent and that we can watch the action of blood flowing in and out of it (Fig. 5.4). First we see the heart at rest and notice **valve flaps** between the atrium and ventricle (the **A-V** valves) on each side of the heart. Blood is pushing down on them from above. Below the flap there is very little pressure, because the heart is relaxed. This means that the pressure of the blood from above pushes the flaps open and fills the ventricle.

Now the muscles in the walls of the heart start pumping. They begin contracting and squeezing the blood in the ventricles. This is the time when we might expect blood to flow back into the veins through which it entered, but as we watch, we notice something happening to the valve flaps. The pressure below the flaps is now much greater than that above. This forces the flaps of the valve toward one another until they close up tight. Blood cannot push its way back into the atria. Instead, it is forced into the arteries. The opening into the arteries is guarded by two other sets of valves, located between the ventricles and their arteries. When the heart was at rest, these valves were closed tight. The pressure in the arteries was greater than the pressure in the ventricles; this kept the valves shut and prevented blood backing up from arteries into the ventricles. (Notice that the flaps of these valves do not hang down into the ventricle like the A-V valves. Instead, they point upward into the arteries.) When the heart makes its pumping stroke, the high pressure of the blood in the ventricle pushes on the flaps of the valves guarding the arteries and forces them open. Blood now flows through the open valves because the pressure of blood in the ventricle is now greater than the pressure in the artery. Each time the valves open and close they produce a sound. These are the sounds you hear when you listen to your heart beat.

Cardiac Output

The amount of blood pumped by the heart is staggering. When you are at complete rest, your heart pumps enough blood to fill four automobile gasoline tanks each hour. Let's break this down into more precise figures. During rest, the heart beats about 70 times per minute. During each beat, each side of the heart pumps roughly 70 ml of blood. The amount of blood pumped during each minute would then equal 70 ml per beat $\times$ 70 beats per minute, or 4900 ml per minute (almost five liters, or $5\frac{1}{4}$ quarts, per minute).

The amount of blood pumped by each side of the heart during each minute is called the **cardiac output.** During activity, the cardiac output changes. When you exercise strenuously, your cardiac output may rise to as much as 25 liters per minute. When a trained athlete exercises, his output may go as high as 40 liters per minute.

The cardiac output is controlled in part by nerves of the autonomic nervous system. Impulses carried by sympathetic nerves to the heart tend to increase cardiac output by increasing both the rate of the heart beat and the strength of each beat. Impulses carried by the parasympathetic nerves to the heart tend to decrease cardiac output by slowing the rate of heart beat.

BLOOD PRESSURE AND BLOOD FLOW

Blood flows from the arteries through the capillaries to the veins because the pressure of blood in the arteries is higher than the pressure of blood in the veins. By the time the blood enters the veins, its pressure has been reduced to only a few millimeters of mercury (mm Hg). This creates a problem because the blood still has a long distance to travel to return to the heart. Furthermore, the veins expand, so blood has a tendency to pool in them.

These difficulties are overcome by a system of valves in the veins themselves, which work in the following way. Any movement you make, particularly a muscular contraction, compresses portions of your veins (Fig. 5.6). The compression squeezes

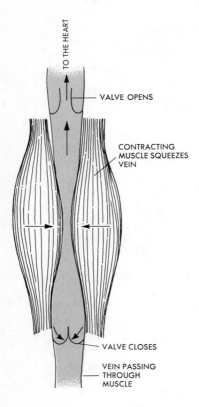

TO THE HEART

VALVE OPENS

CONTRACTING
MUSCLE SQUEEZES
VEIN

VALVE CLOSES

VEIN PASSING
THROUGH
MUSCLE

Fig. 5.6 Contraction of
muscle squeezes the veins,
forcing blood toward the
heart. A closed valve prevents the blood from flowing
backward.

blood out of those portions of the vein and into other portions.
The valves in the veins are arranged like the heart valves and
allow the blood to travel in one direction only. (In Chapter 7
we shall see how respiration also aids venous return. Each time
you breathe in, blood is drawn into the vessels in your chest from
more distant parts of your body.)

All main arteries seem to have about the same average pressure throughout their length. If we think of them as a group,
we might say that they form a blood reservoir maintained at
high pressure by activity of the heart (Fig. 5.7). The extent to
which body tissues draw blood from this reservoir is governed
by the resistance offered by the terminal arteries which lead
into the tissues. These terminal arteries are called **arterioles.**

From moment to moment the pressure in the arterial reservoir pulsates. The pulsation is caused by the heart beat. Each
time the heart contracts it thrusts blood into the arteries. This
expands the arterial reservoir by stretching the elastic walls of
the arteries. An increase in pressure results. When the heart is
relaxed, no blood enters the arteries, but some leaves them
through the arterioles. As a result, the amount of blood in the
arterial reservoir is reduced and the pressure tends to fall. Thus,
with each contraction of the heart the pressure tends to rise,
and during relaxation of the heart the pressure falls. In a healthy,
resting person the blood pressure rises to about 120 mm Hg
during each contraction of the heart. It falls to about 80 mm Hg
each time the heart relaxes. The actual pressure oscillates
between these two figures—80 and 120 mm Hg. (Figure 2.4
shows how arterial pressure could be measured.)

This pulsation can be felt at several points on the surface
of the body—the inner wrist, ankle, and temple—where arteries
are close to the surface. The average pressure is usually about
100 mm Hg, and it is this average pressure that we shall be
concerned with. The amount of blood in the arteries determines
to a large extent the average pressure. If the amount is large,
this means that the arterial walls are stretched and the pressure is high. On the other hand, when the amount is low the
pressure is also low.

Fig. 5.7 Average blood
pressure in the arteries
depends on the inflow and
outflow of the arterial reservoir.

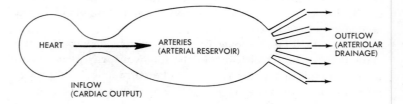

HEART

ARTERIES
(ARTERIAL RESERVOIR)

OUTFLOW
(ARTERIOLAR
DRAINAGE)

INFLOW
(CARDIAC OUTPUT)

The average pressure depends on the inflow and outflow of blood to and from the arterial reservoir. As Fig. 5.7 shows in a schematic way, blood comes in from the heart and leaves through the arterioles. The arterioles are tiny narrow vessels, consequently they offer a good deal of resistance to the passage of blood. Further, their walls are surrounded with smooth muscle. When the muscle contracts, the arterioles constrict and offer even more resistance. Thus, two things govern the amount of blood in the arterial reservoir, and hence the average pressure of the arterial reservoir: 1. The size of the arteriolar passageway can change and thereby alter the resistance to blood flowing out of the reservoir. 2. The cardiac output (inflow to the reservoir) can also change. As a general rule, the amount of blood in the reservoir, and hence the average arterial pressure, increase with an increase in cardiac output (increased inflow), and with an increase in arteriolar resistance (decreased outflow). On the other hand, the pressure decreases if the cardiac output or the arteriolar resistance decrease. This can be summarized by a simple expression:

average arterial pressure = cardiac output × arteriolar resistance

We have already seen that muscles of the heart are controlled by the autonomic nervous system. What controls the smooth muscle in the arterioles? Normally they are partly contracted. When in this state, they can either relax, or contract more. The smooth muscles which control the size of the arterioles are controlled by two things: 1. *Sympathetic nerve impulses*—the smooth muscles are partially contracted because they are normally bombarded by excitatory sympathetic nerve impulses. Increasing the frequency of these impulses causes further contraction, and the arterioles constrict. Decreasing the frequency allows the muscles to relax, and the arterioles dilate. 2. *Metabolic products* such as acids and carbon dioxide also cause a dilation of the blood vessels.

Regulation of Local Blood Flow by Metabolic Products

The regulation of local blood flow by metabolic products provides us with a striking example of a **homeostatic** mechanism. First, let us show that metabolic products affect blood flow by performing a simple demonstration. Suppose a tourniquet is tied around your arm so tightly that it closes off all the blood vessels lying under it. The blood flow to your arm below the level of the tourniquet is stopped completely. When the tourniquet is released, the blood flow to the lower part of your arm does not simply go back to normal; it exceeds the

Fig. 5.8 This negative
feedback loop shows how accumulation of metabolites in
a tissue helps regulate the
tissue's blood supply.

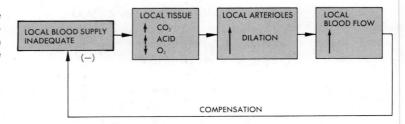

normal level. Although the average arterial pressure does not
change significantly, the blood vessels in the lower part of your
arm have enlarged a bit, thus allowing more than the normal
amount of blood to flow into the stricken region when the
tourniquet is released. This response is advantageous to the
surrounding tissue in the following way. During the period of
cutoff, metabolism continued; waste products were building up
since there was no blood flow to carry them away. Oxygen was
badly needed since none was being delivered. The increase in
blood flow after the tourniquet was removed enabled the cells
to meet their metabolic needs. The question now is "how do the
blood vessels dilate?"

If we cut the nerves leading to the deprived tissues, we could
repeat the demonstration and get exactly the same results. This
tells us that the nerves are not involved in the blood vessel dilation of this experiment. If we take blood from that part of the
arm where the circulation has been cut off, and then inject it
into some other part of the body, we get a startling result. *The
vessels in the area of the injection dilate;* therefore, some substance
produced by the tissue deprived of fresh blood seems to be responsible for the dilation. It turns out that many products of
normal metabolism bring about the action. Carbon dioxide
and acids are among them. Thus, blood vessel dilation stimulated by metabolic products during times of intense activity is an
automatic safeguard assuring that active tissues receive an adequate supply of blood. The local environment of these tissues
is restored and normal metabolism proceeds. The feedback loop
describing this regulation of local blood supply is illustrated in
Fig. 5.8.

Regulation of Blood Pressure

The action of **metabolites** (metabolic products)
on the arteriolar walls provides us with an automatic mechanism for increasing the blood flow through an active tissue. But
this works only if the blood pressure in the arterial reservoir is
high enough to drive the blood. The mechanism fails if the
blood pressure drops too low. On the other hand, an extremely

high blood pressure also has disadvantages. If the blood pressure is too high, the heart has to pump harder to expel its contents each time it beats. Also, a high pressure may be transmitted to the capillaries where it will force fluid out into the tissue spaces. As a result, the tissues swell. Thus, if the blood pressure is either too high or too low, the constancy of the internal environment and survival is threatened. The regulation of blood pressure, so that it remains reasonably constant despite the changing demands of the tissues, provides us with another illustration of the principle of homeostasis.

Actually, we know of more than one mechanism that regulates blood pressure. Of these, one of the most important involves a reflex which has its receptors located in the walls of the aorta and in the walls of branches of the aorta leading to the brain. These branches are called the **carotid arteries** (Fig. 5.9). The receptors are sensitive to stretch. If, for example, the blood pressure is increased, the walls of the aorta and the carotid arteries are stretched, and so are the receptors. Stretching the receptors increases the frequency of impulses on sensory nerves leading from these receptors to a reflex center in the lower part of the brain (the **medulla**). This results in an inhibition of the supply of sympathetic nerve impulses to the heart and the arterioles, together with an excitation of the parasympathetic supply to the heart. In turn, this leads to decreased cardiac output, and dilation of the arterioles, which reduces the resistance to blood flow out of the arteries. Both the decreased cardiac output and the decreased resistance reduce the elevated blood pressure, bringing it back down toward normal. This feedback loop for regulating blood pressure is illustrated in Fig. 5.10.

If the blood pressure is reduced for some reason, the opposite response occurs. The frequency of impulses on sensory nerves leading from the aorta and carotid arteries is reduced. The sympathetic nerve supply to the heart and arterioles is excited.

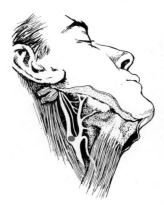

Fig. 5.9 The red dot shows the location of stretch receptors in the wall of the carotid artery. These stretch receptors respond to changes in blood pressure and take part in the feedback loop in Fig. 5.10.

Fig. 5.10 The negative feedback system below shows how the heart and arterioles compensate for an increase in blood pressure. If the blood pressure were *decreased*, the heart and arterioles would again compensate for the change. Can you reconstruct the diagram to show what happens?

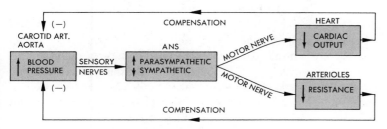

The parasympathetic supply to the heart is inhibited. The cardiac output and arteriolar resistance increase. The blood pressure is raised back toward normal.

The importance of this homeostatic reflex becomes apparent, for example, when a person or animal is injured and loses blood. As blood is lost, the total volume of fluid in the circulatory tree is reduced and the pressure falls. The fall in pressure is minimized by the reflex increase in cardiac activity and blood vessel constriction, which are initiated by receptors in the carotid arteries and aorta. Other compensating adjustments that occur in response to blood loss are revealed when we study the properties of blood itself. These will be discussed in Chapter 6.

SUMMARY

The organs of the body are specialized to perform certain tasks. Each organ produces materials that are carried by the circulating blood to all cells of the body. The blood flow to various organs is adjusted by **homeostatic** mechanisms, with the result that active tissue is provided with an adequate supply of blood.

The circulatory system consists of the heart and a complex network of blood vessels. The direction of blood flow from arteries through the capillaries to the veins is determined by a difference in pressure. The pressure is relatively high in the arteries and low in the veins. The term **blood pressure** refers to the pressure in the main arteries. This pressure pulsates, rising with each beat of the heart and falling during relaxation of the heart. The average pressure in the major arteries depends on two things: **cardiac output** and **arteriolar resistance.**

The cardiac output is controlled by the nerves of the autonomic nervous system. The resistance offered by arterioles is determined by smooth muscles, which control the diameter of the arterioles. These smooth muscles are in turn controlled by *sympathetic nerve impulses* and *metabolic products.* The effect of metabolic products helps to *regulate the local blood supply* so that blood flow through active tissues is increased.

Many mechanisms are involved in the regulation of blood pressure. One of the most important involves a reflex with receptors located in the walls of the **aorta** and in the **carotid** arteries. When the pressure is increased in these areas, the receptors are stimulated so that they send more impulses to the brain. This results in an inhibition of sympathetic nerves leading to the heart and arterioles; it also results in an excitation of parasympathetic nerves leading to the heart. Cardiac output is then decreased and the arterioles are dilated. Both of these factors reduce the elevated blood pressure back toward normal. When the blood pressure drops below normal, the opposite responses occur.

FOR THOUGHT AND DISCUSSION

1 How will the pressure in the arteries compare to the pressure in the veins if the heart stops beating for a long time?

2 If the sympathetic nerves that carry impulses to the hand are cut, what effect will this have on blood flow to the hand? Does it increase or decrease? Explain.

3 If the sensory nerves that carry impulses from the aortic and carotid artery stretch receptors are cut, how will blood pressure be affected? Explain.

4 Heart failure is sometimes caused by damaged heart valves. Sometimes the aortic valve (between the left ventricle and aorta) is damaged and does not close properly. Why would this be a disadvantage? What physiological adjustments might partially overcome the disadvantages?

5 When noradrenalin is placed on an isolated heart, it beats faster. When noradrenalin is injected into an intact animal, the heart rate may increase slightly at first, but very soon after it decreases! Can you offer an explanation for these results? (HINT: consider the inter-relations of noradrenalin, blood pressure, and heart rate.)

SELECTED READINGS

Carlson, A. J., V. Johnson, and H. M. Cavert. *The Machinery of the Body,* 5th Ed. Chicago: University of Chicago Press, 1961.

Harvey, W. *Anatomical Studies on the Motion of the Heart and Blood.* Springfield, Illinois: Charles C. Thomas Publisher, 1931.

Kilgour, F. G. "William Harvey," *Scientific American* (June 1952).

Lillehei, C. W. and L. Engel. "Open-heart Surgery," *Scientific American* (February 1960).

Scher, A. M. "The Electrocardiogram," *Scientific American* (November 1961).

Scholander, P. F. "The Master Switch of Life," *Scientific American* (December 1963) (*Scientific American* reprint #172).

Wiggers, C. J. "The Heart," *Scientific American* (May 1957) (*Scientific American* reprint #62).

Zweifach, B. W. "The Microcirculation of the Blood," *Scientific American* (January 1959) (*Scientific American* reprint #64).

6 BLOOD

In the last chapter we saw some of the ways in which circulation of the blood is controlled. Let us now take a close look at the circulating fluid itself—blood. An average sized adult has about five liters of blood. As blood travels through the circulatory tree, it carries food to the tissues and carries away waste products. Some food stuffs and waste products are simply dissolved in the blood, much as sugar is dissolved in a cup of tea. However, blood is not a simple watery solution. It consists of cells suspended in a clear fluid called **plasma.** These cells, along with some of the proteins dissolved in the plasma, give the blood a number of remarkable properties. Some of these properties are revealed whenever a severe **hemorrhage** (bleeding) occurs.

Soon after bleeding starts, the leak in the cut blood vessel is sealed off with blood that seems to harden, or **clot,** near the

Fig. 6.1 Blood is not a simple watery solution, but is made up of cells suspended in a clear plasma fluid. Both the cells and plasma are specialized to perform a variety of tasks.

Courtesy Dr. W. M. Copenhaver

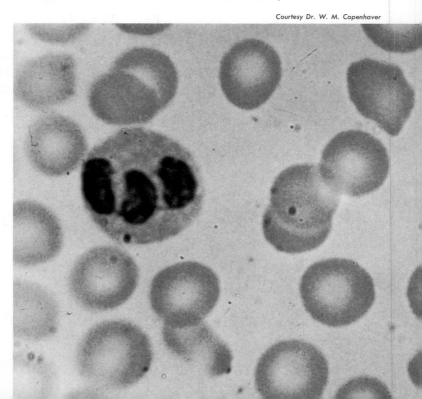

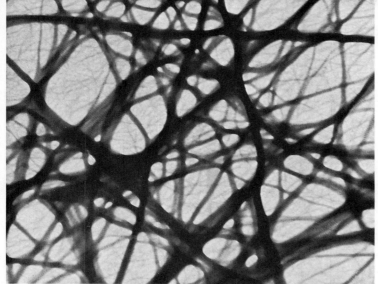

Fig. 6.2 Blood clots are formed by networks of long fibers of fibrin. The network shown in the electronmicrograph above has been magnified 46,000 times.

wound. During the next few hours or so, quite a bit of fluid bathing the tissue cells of the body (extracellular fluid) enters the blood stream. This replaces some of the fluid that was lost during the hemorrhage. Within a few days the lost plasma proteins are replaced. Finally, after a few weeks the number of circulating blood cells returns to normal. In other words, new blood cells have been produced to replace those lost through bleeding. All of these responses help to preserve or restore the internal environment; they are homeostatic responses.

Preventing Loss of Blood

If you cut your hand, it will bleed rapidly at first. Then the bleeding slows down. If the cut is not too deep, the bleeding will probably stop in a few minutes. What causes the blood to stop flowing? The bleeding stops because blood clotted near the wound and sealed the leak. You can demonstrate blood clotting simply by collecting fresh blood in a test tube. If you tip the tube upside down immediately, the blood will flow out. However, if you wait a few minutes before tipping the tube, the blood will not flow out. It is as though you poured some hot gelatin into a test tube and allowed it to cool and set.

We know that as the blood circulates through the body it is not clotted. If the blood does clot, it clogs up important blood vessels, say to the brain, and the results are disastrous. What prevents blood from clotting as it circulates through the body, and yet allows it to clot at the site of a wound?

If we examine a blood clot under a microscope, we find that

63

Fig. 6.3   Three major steps in blood clot formation are shown here. The substances in color are normally present in plasma (or tissues). Thromboplastin and Ca^{++} are necessary for Step 2 to proceed. Thrombin is required for Step 3.

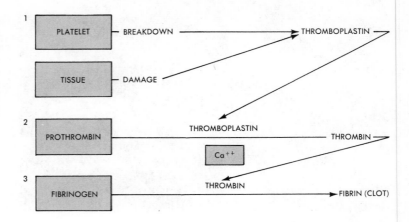

it is composed of a number of threadlike structures entangled in a network (Fig. 6.2). This fibrous network is made up of an insoluble protein called **fibrin.** Blood cells become trapped in the meshes of this network. If we separate the cells from the plasma we still get clot formation. Clotting is a property of plasma and is independent of the cells. Where does fibrin, which forms the clot, come from?

Fibrin is formed from a protein called **fibrinogen** which is dissolved in the plasma. However the formation of fibrin takes place only under special circumstances. A blood clot that forms at a wound, or in a glass test tube, is triggered by the liberation of substances called **thromboplastin.** Thromboplastin is liberated either by injured cells or by the rupture of tiny fragile cell fragments called **platelets,** which are normally present in the blood. The presence of thromboplastin starts a series of reactions producing fibrin from fibrinogen. A simplified outline of this series of reactions is given in Fig. 6.3. You will see from the figure that an important intermediary step in the series of reactions is the conversion of a substance called **prothrombin** into **thrombin.** This step requires free calcium (Ca^{++}), which is normally contained in the blood.

Although most of the substances needed for clotting are normally present in the circulating blood, they are not activated. That is why circulating blood does not clot. It is only when thromboplastin is liberated, and thrombin is formed, that we get clotting. So long as the platelets remain intact they do not rupture and liberate the thromboplastin, which begins the process of clotting. Clot formation occurs in a test tube because the fragile platelets rupture upon contacting glass surfaces. It is possible to prevent clotting by interrupting any one of the steps outlined in Fig. 6.3. Blood banks commonly remove Ca^{++} from the blood, or they block the action of thrombin, to prevent clotting of stored blood. Successful clotting depends on many other substances besides the major ones mentioned here. Some of the substances have only recently been discovered, and quite likely still others remain to be discovered.

Capillary Fluid Exchange

Substances involved in blood clotting make up only a small fraction of the total protein dissolved in the plasma. The entire pool of plasma protein plays an important role in the transfer of fluid across the capillary walls. Fluid can move through the capillary walls in two directions. It can pass from the blood stream into the fluid that bathes body tissues, or it can leave the tissues and enter the blood stream. The pressure of the blood in the capillaries, and the concentration of protein in the blood, govern which way the fluid goes.

Two forces normally balance each other and prevent any net movement of fluid into or out of the capillaries:

1. **BLOOD PRESSURE:** We know that the pumping action of the heart sends blood into the arteries under strong pressure. Although some of this pressure is lost in the arterioles, it is still about 35 mm Hg when it enters the capillaries. By the time the blood leaves the capillaries the pressure has dropped to about 15 mm Hg. Thus, the average pressure in the capillaries is about 25 mm Hg. This pressure is strong enough to force fluid out of the capillaries—which would mean that all of the fluid would drain into the tissue spaces—but a second force prevents such drainage. This second force is osmotic pressure.

2. **OSMOTIC PRESSURE:** As you saw in Chapter 2, when one region has a higher osmotic pressure than another, it tends to draw fluid toward it. If we examine the chemical composition of the extracellular tissue fluids and of the plasma, we find that they are almost identical, except for large protein molecules found in the plasma. The capillary walls are easily permeable to all of the substances dissolved in the blood except for these huge proteins. The proteins keep the osmotic pressure of the blood plasma in the capillaries higher than the osmotic pressure in the tissues. This means that fluid is drawn into the capillaries by osmotic pressure. The magnitude of the osmotic pressure exerted by the plasma proteins is about 25 mm Hg.

The two forces—blood pressure, which tends to push fluid out of the capillaries, and osmotic pressure, which tends to draw fluid into the capillaries—are thus kept in balance. So long as these two forces are equal, there is no net fluid movement. This means that the tissues do not swell or shrink. Actually, at the

Fig. 6.4 This diagram shows why there is no net exchange of fluid (protein-free plasma) between capillaries and surrounding tissue spaces. Because blood pressure at the arterial end of the capillary (colored arrow) is greater than the osmotic pressure (shorter black arrow), fluid leaks out of the capillary into the tissue space. At the venous end of the capillary the osmotic pressure is greater than the blood pressure in the capillary, hence there is movement of fluid into the capillary. The amount of fluid lost and regained by the capillary and tissue space is equal, hence a steady state is maintained.

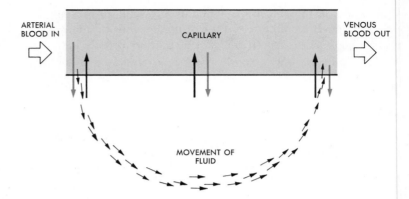

ARTERIAL BLOOD IN

CAPILLARY

VENOUS BLOOD OUT

MOVEMENT OF FLUID

arteriole end of the capillaries the blood pressure is a little higher than the average, so some fluid does seep out into the tissue spaces. However, at the venous end of the capillaries, the blood pressure is lower than the osmotic pressure, and an equivalent amount of fluid tends to seep back into the capillaries. This means that there is no net movement of fluid; the fluids in the tissue space are in a **steady state.** (See Fig. 6.4.)

During hemorrhage, when a large volume of blood is lost, this balance is upset. The volume of blood goes down, which means that the pressure also drops. In turn, this means that the force pushing the blood out of the capillaries is weakened. However, the osmotic pressure—the pressure drawing fluid from the tissues into the capillaries—does not drop. This is because immediately after the hemorrhage the *concentration* of plasma proteins in the circulating blood remains the same. Although there is less blood circulating, it is just as concentrated as before the hemorrhage.

The force drawing fluid from the tissues into the capillaries is now greater than the force pushing fluid out of the capillaries into the tissues. Thus, fluid begins to move from the tissue spaces into the capillaries. This fluid helps to make up for the volume of blood lost during hemorrhage. When the volume has built up toward normal, the plasma proteins are then less concentrated. This means that the osmotic pressure drops so that a balance is again brought about between the blood pressure and the osmotic pressure. Net fluid transfer across the capillaries again comes to a virtual standstill.

During inflammation, and in some allergic reactions, the walls of the capillaries become leaky and permit plasma proteins to pass through. The proteins leak out into the tissue spaces and carry fluid with them. In other words, the osmotic pressure difference across the capillary wall drops and, since the blood pressure remains the same, it forces fluid into the tissue spaces. The result is a swelling of the tissues.

The Lymphatic System

Normally, some protein does leak out very slowly from the capillaries to the tissue spaces. Although the leak is slow, if continued indefinitely the difference in protein osmotic pressure across the capillary membrane would vanish and the blood pressure would force fluid from the circulatory system into the tissue spaces. This does not happen because the small amount of protein that leaks into tissue spaces is continually drained off by a system of thin vessels called **lymphatics** (Fig. 6.5).

The lymphatics originate in nearly all tissue spaces. They are very tiny tube structures which join into larger and larger vessels. They finally lead to the neck region where they drain into the venous system (Fig. 6.5). The lymphatic system contains one-way valves similar to those in the veins. The transport of fluid through the lymphatic system is in many ways similar to the transport of fluid in the venous system. But flow through the lymph system is very slow compared with flow through the circulatory system. Nevertheless, it is sufficient to keep the fluid in the tissue spaces in a steady state, draining off the small amount of protein that may leak out of the capillaries, and draining off other foreign bodies that enter the tissue spaces. Fig. 6.6 shows an example of tissue swelling resulting from deficient lymphatic drainage.

All along the lymph system are a number of enlargements called **nodes.** These important structures are responsible for the filtering out of foreign particles. Specialized cells, called **phagocytes,** are able to engulf and remove foreign particles from the lymph fluid, thus preventing them from entering the general

Armed Forces Institute of Pathology

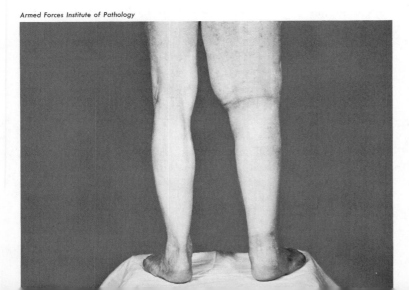

Fig. 6.5 The lymphatic system is constantly but slowly draining fluids (and protein) from the tissue spaces and carrying them to the circulatory system. Enlargements called *nodes* filter out and destroy foreign particles in the fluids. The lymphatic fluid enters the veins at two sites in the neck region.

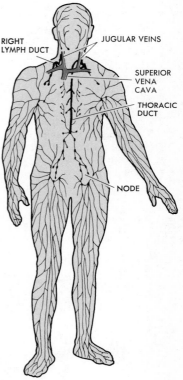

RIGHT LYMPH DUCT

JUGULAR VEINS

SUPERIOR VENA CAVA

THORACIC DUCT

NODE

Fig. 6.6 When the lymphatic system fails, the body tissues swell. Note the swelling which has resulted from impaired lymphatic drainage in the right leg.

circulatory system. In addition, the lymph tissue (as well as white blood cells, spleen, and bone marrow) produces substances called **antibodies.** Antibodies also play a role in the control of foreign particles.

Antibodies

Whenever bacteria or foreign proteins find their way into the body they stimulate the production of antibodies. Particular kinds of antibodies react with particular kinds of invading particles, neutralizing or destroying the invading particles.

Some of the plasma proteins (**globulin**) are antibodies. They react with the invading particles (called **antigens**) in such a way that the antigen no longer has any harmful action. This inactivation may take any one of several forms. It may make the particle insoluble, or it may make it more susceptible to engulfment (**phagocytosis**) and subsequent digestion by other cells. Or if the protein (antigen) with which the antibody reacts is attached to a cell, it may cause these cells to clump together or to disrupt. These antibody reactions are responsible for immunity to many diseases.

These same reactions are also one of the chief difficulties that stand in the way of transplanting tissue—a skin graft, for example—from one person to another. Apparently, when tissue is transplanted the donor cells are recognized by the host as being "foreign" to the host's body. Antibodies specific for the donor cells are then produced by the host and react with the donor cells and destroy them.

The problem of antibody reactions must be dealt with whenever blood transfusions are made. If a person is given the wrong type of blood, antibodies in the plasma of the recipient react with antigens of the donor's blood cells. When they do, the cells of the donor's blood clump together. This clumping, called **agglutination,** can lead to severe illness or death of the person receiving the blood transfusion.

Differing Blood Types

There are several types of antigens that may be present on the donor's red blood cells. Such antigens form the basis for classification of blood types. Two of the antigens are called simply **A** and **B**. Red blood cells may have either A or B, both, or neither antigen. If your red cells contain both antigens, then you have type **AB** blood. If they contain only the A antigen, then you have type **A** blood; if only the B antigen, type **B**. If

Fig. 6.7 Schematic diagram of blood cell antigens and plasma antibodies that correspond to different blood group types.

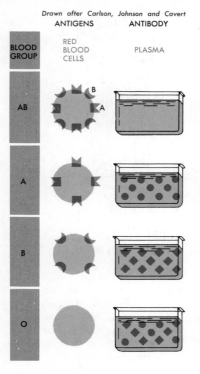

they do not contain either of the antigens, then you have type **O** blood.

A person whose blood type is AB does not have any antibodies for either the A or the B antigen in his plasma. If he did, these antibodies would react with the antigens and cause the cells to agglutinate, and he would not survive. Similarly, a person whose blood type is A cannot have the A antibody in his plasma, but he may, and usually does, have the B antibody. A person whose blood type is B has only the A antibody. And, finally, the person whose blood type is O usually has both the A and the B antibodies in his plasma. No reaction occurs here because there is no antigen on his red blood cells.

Suppose we want to transfuse blood into a person whose type is B. We must assume that he has A antibodies in his plasma. This means that he cannot receive blood from anyone who has the A antigen on his red cells. In other words, he cannot receive blood cells from a donor of type A or of type AB. However, he can receive blood from a person with the same blood type (type B) or from a donor whose blood type is O. Using the same arguments, we see that a person with type A blood can receive cells from another person whose blood type is either A or O. A person whose blood type is AB has no antibodies in his plasma, so he can receive blood from any of the types A, B, AB, or O. Finally, a person whose blood type is O has both antibodies in his plasma. Consequently, he can receive blood only from a type O donor. The A and B antigens are not the only ones carried by red blood cells. Sometimes, although less frequently, reactions that do not involve A and B antigens occur. Figure 6.8 shows the clumping reactions that occur when red cells are placed in different plasma types.

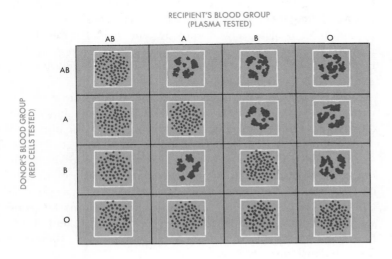

RECIPIENT'S BLOOD GROUP
(PLASMA TESTED)

AB   A   B   O

DONOR'S BLOOD GROUP
(RED CELLS TESTED)

AB

A

B

O

Fig. 6.8 This figure shows reactions that take place when different types of blood are mixed.

BLOOD CELLS

There are several kinds of cells in the circulating blood. Those that have little or no color are collectively called white blood cells. The white blood cells play an important role in the removal of foreign particles. They accomplish this in several ways. For example, some white blood cells are capable of engulfing foreign particles or bacteria (Fig. 6.9). In an infected wound, such cells tend to accumulate near the infected region and take up bacteria and dead tissue. Once inside the white cell, the bacteria and dead tissue are broken down. These white cells are limited in the number of particles they can engulf, and eventually they die. Pus that accumulates near a wound consists largely of dead white cells. Other white cells are involved in the production of specific antibodies which react with foreign particles or bacteria and inactivate them.

The red cells in the circulating blood are almost 1000 times more numerous than white blood cells and are responsible for the red color of blood. The red color is due to an iron-containing protein called **hemoglobin,** which makes up about 30 per cent of the weight of the red blood cell. Hemoglobin is very important in the carriage of oxygen, carbon dioxide, and acid by the blood. These matters will be discussed in the next chapter.

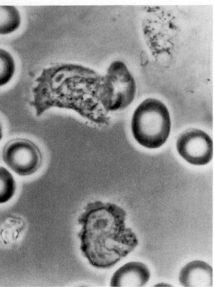

Lester V. Bergman and Associates, Inc.

Fig. 6.9 Some white blood cells are capable of engulfing foreign particles. The process is called *phagocystosis.*

SUMMARY

Blood consists of red and white blood cells suspended in a liquid called **plasma.** White blood cells play an important role by removing foreign particles from the blood. Red blood cells contain **hemoglobin,** a protein that is very important in the transport of oxygen, carbon dioxide, and acid by the blood. Proteins that are dissolved in the plasma play an important role in blood clotting, in the exchange of fluid across capillary walls, and in antigen-antibody reactions.

Blood clots that form near a wound are made from a fibrous network of an insoluble protein called **fibrin.** The blood clot forms as a result of a series of reactions initiated by the liberation of **thromboplastin** from injured tissue or **platelets.**

The fluid exchanged between the capillaries and the tissue spaces is governed by two forces: capillary blood pressure and osmotic pressure of the plasma proteins. The blood pressure tends to force fluid out of the capillaries and into the tissue spaces; osmotic pressure exerted by the plasma proteins tends to move fluid in the opposite direction. Normally, these two forces balance one another.

When **antigens** gain entry into the body, they stimulate the production of **antibodies.** The antibodies react with the antigens and destroy or inactivate the antigens. These antigen-antibody reactions are responsible for immunity to many diseases. Incompatible blood transfusions result from antigen-antibody reactions if the antibodies in the plasma of the recipient react with the antigens of the donor's blood cells and cause them to **agglutinate.**

FOR THOUGHT AND DISCUSSION

1 During an accident, a large blood vessel is cut and bleeding is severe. What are the threats to survival? Outline the physiological responses that will help the person survive.

2 In some forms of heart failure the left side of the heart is the weakest and fails to perform properly while the right side continues to pump blood into the lungs with near normal vigor. Under these conditions fluid flows from the lung capillaries into the spaces of the lungs, resulting in a condition called *pulmonary edema.* Explain. (HINT: What do you think happens to the blood pressure in the lung capillaries under these conditions?)

3 During starvation, there may be inadequate formation of plasma proteins. Would you expect tissue spaces to swell or shrink?

4 A clever student, who knows he has blood type B, is given eight red blood cell suspensions and the *serum* (blood plasma in which fibrinogen has been removed) from each sample. He manages to identify each of the four blood types present. To test these samples, the only materials he has at his disposal are his own blood cells and his own serum. How did he make the identifications? Why was serum used instead of plasma?

SELECTED READINGS

Burnet, Sir McFarlane. "The Mechanism of Immunity," *Scientific American* (January 1961) (*Scientific American* reprint #78).

Carlson, A. J., V. Johnson, and H. M. Cavert. *The Machinery of the Body,* 5th Ed. Chicago: University of Chicago Press, 1961.

Guyton, A. C. *Textbook of Medical Physiology,* 3rd Ed. Philadelphia: W. B. Saunders Co., 1966.

Mayerson, H. S. "The Lymphatic System," *Scientific American* (June 1963) (*Scientific American* reprint #158).

Zucker, M. B. "Blood Platelets," *Scientific American* (February 1961).

7 OXYGEN

We live at the bottom of a great sea of air composed mostly of the gases nitrogen and oxygen. As we move through it, we constantly exchange materials with the air. Because this great reservoir of air has been present on the Earth all during the evolution of man, the human body was able to evolve without developing special storage depots for oxygen. Storage depots are necessary when an essential substance, sugar, say, is not always available.

The action of breathing is the major way in which we constantly exchange materials with the air around us, our external environment. Breathing movements keep the air in our lungs thoroughly mixed with the atmosphere. In turn, the air in our lungs is in close contact with blood contained in capillaries of the pulmonary circulation.

The act of breathing is only one link in the chain of events enabling us to use oxygen. We must also consider the problem of how the blood carries enough oxygen to satisfy the demands of our numerous body tissues. If oxygen were simply dissolved in plasma, as sugar dissolves in water, the amount of oxygen carried by the blood would be inadequate. We shall see that red blood cells increase the capacity of blood to carry oxygen 70 times. We must also ask why oxygen is essential, and what are some of the homeostatic mechanisms that adjust the supply of oxygen to the changing demands of body tissues.

How We Breathe

Although air enters our bodies through the nose and mouth, and travels down the windpipe (**trachea**), it is not until it reaches the lungs that the real exchange of gases between our bodies and the external environment takes place. The trachea is divided in two, and each division subdivides several more times. The subdivisions end in tiny dead end sacs called

THE RESPIRATORY SYSTEM

Fig. 7.1   Breathing is the major way in which we constantly exchange materials with the air around us. During inspiration, air moves into the body through the nose and mouth, passes through the trachea and its branches (bronchi and bronchioles, shown at lower right), into the alveoli, (lower left), which are tiny sac-like structures in close proximity to capillaries. It is here that oxygen diffuses into the blood and carbon dioxide diffuses out. The cycle of breathing is completed during expiration, when carbon dioxide and other gases are expelled from the alveoli, travel through the respiratory passages, and are emptied into the atmosphere.

 1 TONGUE

 2 PHARYNX

 3 EPIGLOTTIS

 4 LARYNX

 5 ESOPHAGUS

 6 TRACHEA

 7 BRONCHUS

 8 LUNGS

 9 BRONCHIOLE

10 ALVEOLUS

11 PULMONARY ARTERIOLE

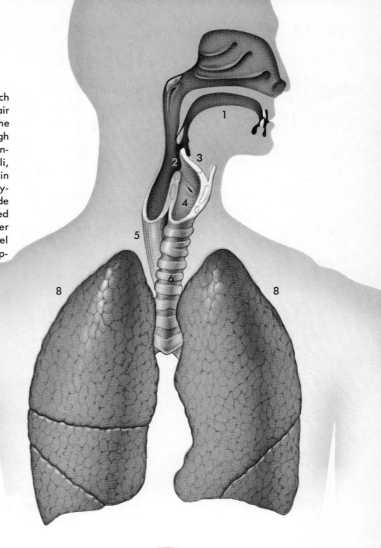

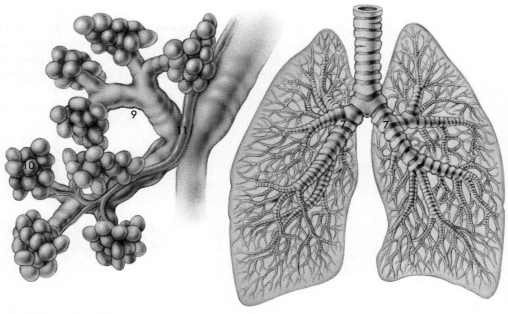

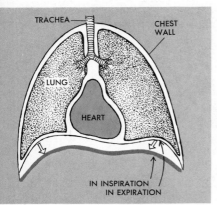

TRACHEA

CHEST WALL

LUNG

HEART

IN INSPIRATION
IN EXPIRATION

Redrawn from Carlson, Johnson, and Cavert

Fig. 7.2 Breathing involves a rhythmic change in the volume of the chest cage. The diaphragm acts like a piston that moves up and down. During the downward movement (contraction), air is drawn into the lungs; during upward movement (relaxation), air is forced out.

alveoli (Fig. 7.1). Alveoli have very thin walls and a rich supply of blood capillaries. Thus, air in the alveoli is brought in very close contact with capillary blood, enabling a rapid exchange between alveolar air and blood to take place.

The act of breathing maintains a supply of fresh air in the alveoli of the lungs. Each time we inhale, the lungs expand and suck in air. Each time we exhale, the lungs contract and push out air. What is responsible for this rhythmic expansion and contraction of the lungs? We know that the lungs do not contain any muscle tissue. If we open the chest of an animal to look at the lungs, we find that they are collapsed. With the chest open, the lungs remain collapsed despite the fact that the animal continues its breathing movements. The animal's chest cage expands and contracts rhythmically just as though it were breathing normally. Nevertheless the lungs do not move. Apparently the breathing movements are due to muscles which are not directly connected to the lungs.

If we look closely, we find that they are due to movements of muscles connected to the rib cage, and due to a large sheet of muscle called the **diaphragm** which separates the chest cavity from the abdominal cavity.

Figure 7.2 is a diagram of the chest with the right and left lungs inside the chest wall and the diaphragm below. We can think of the chest cavity as a closed box. The lungs are like two balloons, connected at the neck. The neck of the balloon would be the trachea, which allows air to pass into or out of the chest cavity. The diaphragm acts as a piston which can move up or down. When the diaphragm is relaxed, it assumes a curved dome position and rests up against the bottom of the lungs. When it contracts, its curvature decreases and it moves downward, just as a piston would (Fig. 7.2). This creates a partial vacuum in the closed box (and in the lungs). Since the pressure in the lungs is now reduced, air moves from the outside (high pressure) into the lungs (low pressure). This is the intake of breath (**inspiration**). The diaphragm then relaxes. In doing so, it pushes up against the lungs, causing them to expel air to the outside.

Muscles connected to the rib cage also expand and contract the volume of the chest cage. The ribs are attached to the spinal column by hinge-like joints which allow them to move up and down. During relaxation of the rib muscles, the ribs are slanted downward (Fig. 7.3). When the muscles contract the rib cage is pulled upward in a more horizontal position. You can see from the figure that this motion will increase the volume of the chest cage.

Thus, when we breathe in, the rib cage expands because the muscles attached to the ribs pull the ribs upward, and the diaphragm contracts, lowering the floor of the chest cage. As a result, air moves into the lungs. When we exhale (**expiration**) the rib and diaphragm muscles relax, the diaphragm goes back to its original dome shape, pushing up against the lungs, and the ribs drop back into place. As a result, the size of the chest cage decreases and air is pushed out of the lungs. During rest, expiration results from the simple passive relaxation of the diaphragm and rib muscles. However, during strenuous breathing, air can be expelled more forcibly from the lungs by contraction of another set of rib muscles, which pull the rib cage down (to a smaller volume).

What is responsible for the rhythmic activity of the rib and diaphragm muscles? Apparently, the contraction of muscles during respiration is completely controlled by the nervous system. If we cut the motor nerves leading to the diaphragm and ribs of an experimental animal, respiration ceases immediately. Contrast this with the heart, which continues to beat in the absence of any nerve supply.

Nerve impulses that stimulate breathing movements come from regions in the lower parts of the brain (the **medulla**). These regions are called **respiratory centers.** If these centers are destroyed, breathing ceases immediately. If we stimulate certain areas within these centers, prolonged inspiration results. If other areas in the centers are stimulated, prolonged expiration takes place. These respiratory centers send out patterns of nerve impulses to the diaphragm and rib muscles. The result is a regular pattern of inspiration followed by expiration.

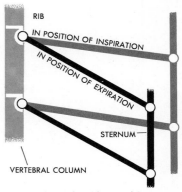

Redrawn from Carlson, Johnson, and Cavert

Fig. 7.3 While the diaphragm expands the rib cage in a vertical direction, the upward movement of ribs expands the cage in a horizontal direction.

Oxygen Transport

The concentration of oxygen in blood entering the lungs is low because the blood has just come from other parts of the body which have extracted substantial amounts of oxygen from it. On the other hand, the concentration of oxygen in the alveolar air is relatively high because it is flushed with fresh air with each breath. As a result, oxygen diffuses from alveolar air (high concentration) to capillary blood (low concentration). In the process, oxygen is dissolved in the blood plasma.

The amount of oxygen that can be dissolved in plasma is severely limited and cannot possibly supply the needs of the body. However, once oxygen enters the plasma, it passes readily into the red blood cells where it becomes loosely attached to **hemoglobin** molecules. Hemoglobin performs a vital function in getting oxygen to the tissues of the body. We can think of each hemoglobin molecule as a large mass containing four sites, or positions, where oxygen can be attached. If the concentration of oxygen in contact with hemoglobin is high, nearly all of the sites will be filled with oxygen. In this case, any particular oxygen molecule can shake loose from the hemoglobin. But, since the oxygen concentration in the surrounding fluid is also high, there is always an oxygen molecule waiting to take the place of one that becomes dislodged. On the other hand, if the oxygen concentration is low, there are very few oxygen molecules available to take the place of any that come loose. In this case, then, many of the hemoglobin sites are unoccupied by oxygen.

Blood leaving the lungs, where it has been in contact with a high concentration of oxygen, has about 99 per cent of its hemoglobin sites filled with oxygen. From the lungs, the oxygen-rich blood enters the left heart and is then pumped to the various body organs. All organs consume oxygen. As a result, the oxygen concentration in the tissues is low. Oxygen diffuses from the plasma directly to the tissue cells. This lowers the plasma oxygen concentration, so additional oxygen is now released by hemoglobin. By far most oxygen consumed by tissue is transported by hemoglobin, not by blood plasma. In order to complete our story, we must at this point ask a basic question: *Why* do the cells need oxygen?

The Role of Oxygen

A cell's need for oxygen is directly linked to the capacity of the cell to use the chemical energy stored in foods. This energy enables muscle contraction, active transport, the building of cellular structure, and other processes to take place. Energy is released from cellular foods (such as glucose) when the foods are broken down into smaller molecules. The most complete and efficient breakdown requires oxygen. The net result can be represented as follows:

$$C_6H_{12}O_6 + 6O_2 \rightarrow 6CO_2 + 6H_2O + energy \begin{cases} ATP \\ Heat \end{cases}$$

1 glucose + 6 oxygen   6 carbon + 6 water
dioxide

The actual chemical reactions that take place in cells are more complicated than our simple representation indicates. For instance, the glucose is split apart in several steps. In the process, hydrogen atoms are stripped off the glucose molecule, and eventually they are transferred to oxygen, resulting in the formation of water. The role of oxygen is simply to remove the hydrogen. During this process a sizable portion of released energy is again stored—but this time through the formation of ATP (see Chapter 3).

In the absence of oxygen, glucose can still be broken down,

but only partially because there is no longer any substantial means for removal of hydrogen. Instead of forming CO_2 as an end product, a partial breakdown product, **lactic acid** ($C_3H_6O_3$), is formed. The release of energy in this case is less complete and far less efficient. In the absence of oxygen the partial breakdown of glucose yields only about 6 per cent of the ATP that is normally produced during complete breakdown in the presence of oxygen.

During the complete breakdown of glucose in the presence of oxygen, for each molecule of oxygen that is used, one molecule of CO_2 and one molecule of H_2O are formed. In addition to glucose, cells can use other foods (such as proteins or fat) for energy. However, the same pattern emerges: oxygen is consumed, ATP, CO_2, and H_2O are produced. The amount of water formed by this process is no problem because it is very small compared with the large amounts normally contained within the cells. But the formation of CO_2 *does* present a problem. The CO_2 must be removed. The problems of oxygen usage and CO_2 removal, then, are very closely linked.

Transport of Carbon Dioxide

The concentration of CO_2 is higher in the cells than in the capillary blood stream, simply because CO_2 is constantly being produced in the cells. When CO_2 diffuses from the cells into the blood, only a small amount of it (about 9 per cent) reaching the blood is held in simple solution. Another fraction (about 27 per cent) attaches directly to the hemoglobin. The remaining (major) portion (64 per cent) combines with water, forming bicarbonate ions and hydrogen ions.

Hydrogen ions are very reactive. They are responsible for the very strong chemical activity of acids. Normally the amount of hydrogen ions in blood is tiny—about 0.00000004 gram per liter. Any substantial increase or decrease in this concentration is fatal. Each time blood passes through the tissues, it picks up large quantities of carbon dioxide. This then reacts with water, forming **bicarbonate** (HCO_3^-) and **hydrogen** (H^+) **ions.** If the story ended here, each time the blood passed through tissues its free hydrogen ion content would increase intolerably. The free hydrogen ions must be removed in some way.

There are many substances in the blood capable of binding the excess free hydrogen ions. Hemoglobin is one of the most important of these substances. Hydrogen ions, oxygen, and hemoglobin interact in a remarkable way so that just the "right thing" seems to happen at just the "right time." When hydrogen ions combine with hemoglobin, the hemoglobin releases some

Fig. 7.4 This diagram shows chemical interactions that take place in the blood as oxygen and carbon dioxide are exchanged between capillaries and cells. Reactions 2 and 3 take place inside red blood cells. The products HCO_3^- and HHb are carried to the lungs by the venous blood.

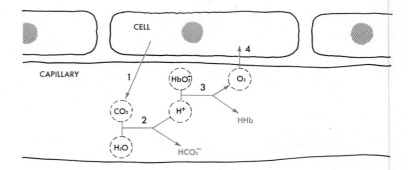

of the oxygen attached to it. Conversely, when oxygen combines with hemoglobin, the hemoglobin releases some of the hydrogen attached to it.

With the aid of Fig. 7.4, let us follow the details as blood passes through a tissue:

1. Carbon dioxide is produced in the cells of the tissue and diffuses into the plasma and into the blood cells.

2. Blood cells contain an enzyme (**carbonic anhydrase**) which accelerates the reaction of CO_2 and H_2O. As a result, the CO_2 combines with H_2O, forming bicarbonate (HCO_3^-) and hydrogen (H^+) ions.

3. Most of the released H^+ is taken up by the combined form of oxygen and hemoglobin which is called **oxy-hemoglobin** (HbO_2^-). The oxy-hemoglobin is present in blood arriving at the tissue. The binding of H^+ by HbO_2^- aids in the release of O_2 by HbO_2^-.

4. Oxygen diffuses into the tissue cells where it is consumed. Thus, we see that free H^+ does not accumulate because it is bound to the hemoglobin.

The blood leaving the tissues contains large quantities of HCO_3^- and large quantities of hemoglobin which is free of oxygen and is called **reduced hemoglobin** (HHb). No further changes take place until the blood reaches the capillaries of the lungs. Details of the changes taking place in the lungs are illustrated in Fig. 7.5 as follows:

Fig. 7.5 Chemical interactions that take place in the blood as oxygen and carbon dioxide are exchanged between capillaries and the lungs are shown here. Reactions 2 and 3 take place inside the red blood cells. The product HbO_2^- is carried to the tissues by arterial blood.

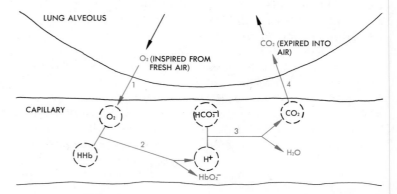

1. The concentration of oxygen in the lung alveoli is high because of breathing movements. The O_2 diffuses from the alveoli into the plasma and blood cells.

2. The O_2 combines with HHb to form HbO_2^-, and this releases H^+.

3. The H^+ combines with HCO_3^- and forms H_2O and CO_2.

4. The CO_2 diffuses into the lung alveoli where it is expelled in the process of normal breathing.

Again, H^+ does not accumulate, because as soon as it is released from HHb it combines with HCO_3^- which releases CO_2. Hemoglobin is essential because it serves as a carrier within the circulation for O_2, CO_2, and H^+.

Control of Oxygen Delivery

The demands of the tissue for oxygen are not always the same. During exercise, for example, you need more energy, and your tissues consume more oxygen than when you are at rest. In addition to the changing demands of the tissue, there are times when the supply of oxygen from the external environment changes. If you climb a mountain the air becomes "thinner" and the concentration of oxygen reaching the lung alveoli is reduced. Nevertheless, the cells of the body require just as much oxygen at the top of a mountain as they do at its base. How does the body adjust to variations in supply and demand of oxygen?

The amount of oxygen delivered to the cells can be altered by the body in two ways: 1. *The amount of blood reaching the tissue may be changed.* If each ml of blood has the same amount of oxygen dissolved in it, and if the blood flow to the tissue is doubled, then the amount of oxygen delivered to the tissue will also double. We saw examples of changes in local blood flow in Chapter 5. 2. A second method of altering the amount of oxygen delivered to the tissue is *to alter the amount of oxygen contained in each ml. of blood.* If the amount of blood reaching a tissue does not change, but if the concentration of oxygen in the blood doubles, then the total amount of oxygen delivered to the tissue will also double.

In this chapter we are concerned primarily with *regulation* of the oxygen delivery through regulation of the oxygen concentration in the blood. Regulation of the oxygen concentration can be brought about in two ways.

1. The concentration of oxygen in the blood can be altered by *changing the concentration of oxygen in the air* that is in direct contact with the blood in the alveoli of the lungs. This can be accomplished by changes in the rate and depth of breathing.

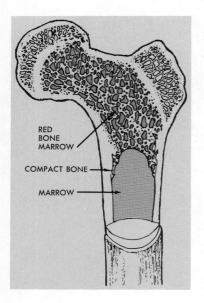

RED BONE MARROW

COMPACT BONE

MARROW

Fig. 7.6 Since the average life-span of a red blood cell is about 120 days, these cells must constantly be replaced. Red bone marrow is the site of formation of the red cells.

When you increase your rate and depth of breathing, you bring about a more efficient mixing of the alveolar air with the air of the external environment. As a result, the oxygen content of alveolar air increases. An increase in breathing is an important response when body tissues become active and demand more and more oxygen from the blood. The oxygen-poor venous blood returning to the lungs, in turn, requires more and more oxygen from the alveoli. Unless you increase your breathing rate, the alveolar oxygen concentration will fall and be unable to supply your body's needs.

2. The capacity of blood to take up oxygen can be altered by a *change in the amount of hemoglobin* in each ml of blood. This can be brought about by a *change in the number of red blood cells* in each ml of blood. Let us consider this latter possibility in some detail.

Regulation of Hemoglobin—The Life of the Red Cell

The average red blood cell stays in the circulation for only about 120 days before it is destroyed in the liver, spleen, or bone. This means that $\frac{1}{120}$ or almost 1 per cent of all the body's red blood cells are destroyed each day! Yet, under normal circumstances, the number of these cells in the circulation does not change; that is, they are in a steady state. It follows that new cells must be produced and added to the circulation just as fast as old cells are destroyed.

Where do the new cells come from, and how is their production rate geared to the body's need for oxygen? Since red blood cells do not have a nucleus, they certainly cannot divide and form new cells. Rather, they are formed from nucleated cells found in the interior of bones—in the **bone marrow** (Fig. 7.6). In the adult this takes place mainly in the vertebrae, and in bones of the chest, skull, and pelvis.

The rate of production of red cells (and, consequently, of hemoglobin) is not rigidly fixed. It depends on the oxygen con-

Fig. 7.7 Red blood cell production is stimulated by a lack of oxygen. The feedback loop shows how this response helps maintain the oxygen content in the blood.

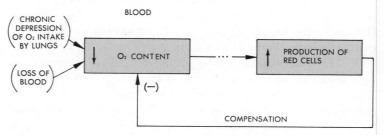

tent of the blood. Whenever the oxygen content of blood is low, the production rate of red cells increases. This provides the body with an effective homeostatic mechanism for regulation of blood oxygen. The feedback loop for this process is illustrated in Fig. 7.7.

When you climb a mountain, for example, as you go higher the air becomes less dense. This means that less and less oxygen is reaching your lungs, so the oxygen content in the blood falls. You find yourself short of breath. However, after a few weeks of living at high altitude, a process of acclimatization sets in. You are more comfortable. Why? Each ml of your blood contains a greater number of red cells and, therefore, a greater concentration of hemoglobin which can carry oxygen. The oxygen content of the blood has risen back toward normal. We account for this by the scheme illustrated in Fig. 7.7. The decreased blood oxygen stimulated an increase in the rate of red cell production.

Another example is found in the body's response to severe bleeding. Red cells are lost, which means that the capacity of blood to carry oxygen is decreased. The resulting decrease in oxygen content stimulates red cell production, which compensates for the original loss.

It is important to emphasize that this response (increased red cell production) to a decreased oxygen content is a slow one. It takes many days before the increased cell production fully compensates for the low oxygen state. Although this long-term adjustment is essential, the body tissues cannot wait for days before the oxygen delivery returns to normal. A quicker response is necessary. This is accomplished by an increase in the amount of blood flowing to the tissues (see Chapter 5) and an increase in breathing.

Control of Breathing

Whenever your cells become unusually active, you breathe faster. This provides the extra oxygen needed by the more active tissues and expels the excess CO_2 that has been produced. But what is responsible for the increase in breathing when the tissues become more active? In other words, why do the muscles involved in breathing (diaphragm and rib muscles) become more active when other parts of the body begin consuming more oxygen?

Since the blood O_2 and CO_2 are controlled by breathing, it is reasonable to ask whether or not blood O_2 and CO_2, in turn, have any influence on breathing. In other words, is there any simple control loop involving breathing and O_2 and CO_2? The answer is yes in both cases. A *low* concentration of O_2 and

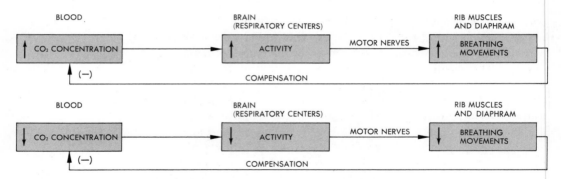

Fig. 7.8 The level of carbon dioxide in the blood is of primary importance in regulating breathing. A high concentration of carbon dioxide stimulates breathing. This response reduces carbon dioxide concentration back toward normal (top diagram). A low concentration of carbon dioxide decreases breathing. This response increases the carbon dioxide concentration back toward normal (bottom diagram).

a *high* concentration of CO_2 both stimulate breathing. The increase in concentration of CO_2 in blood carried to the brain acts directly on the medulla. The respiratory centers respond by discharging a greater number of motor nerve impulses to the rib muscles and diaphragm. This produces an increase in breathing movements, more CO_2 is expelled, and more O_2 may be picked up by the blood. This homeostatic response, which guards against large changes in CO_2 concentrations in the body fluids is summarized in Fig. 7.8. For example, this response prevents you from holding your breath for an indefinite period. While you hold your breath, CO_2 is not removed from your body. Its concentration quickly builds up and it begins to stimulate respiration so strongly that you are no longer able to hold your breath—you gasp for air.

The breathing response to a low oxygen concentration differs in detail from the response to CO_2. Unlike CO_2, O_2 does not act *directly* on the brain. Instead, it acts on special nerve receptors called **chemoreceptors,** which are located near the aortic arch and carotid sinus (close to the pressure receptors responsible for regulating blood pressure). The chemoreceptors are stimulated by low O_2 concentrations. Nerve impulses are sent to

Fig. 7.9 A low concentration of oxygen in the blood stimulates breathing. The feedback loop shows how this response guards against serious lowering of the concentration of oxygen.

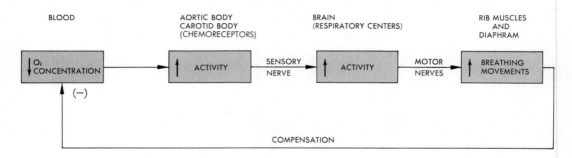

the respiratory centers, which in turn send more motor nerve impulses to the muscles controlling breathing. As a result, breathing movements are increased and we have a homeostatic reflex which specifically guards against low O_2 concentrations. The feedback loop is shown in Fig. 7.9. This reflex operates when you climb a mountain. The higher you go, the more you breathe. The chemoreceptor reflex is responsible for the rapid breathing.

Although the concentrations of O_2 and CO_2 both influence breathing, under normal conditions the response to CO_2 is much stronger. It is only when the level of O_2 is greatly lowered that O_2 begins to play a role.

In addition to O_2 and CO_2 levels, there are other factors that influence your breathing. For example, you can breathe faster any time you choose, so the respiratory centers must be influenced by higher centers of the brain. We have found it difficult to locate and sort out the relative importance of all of the factors that control breathing. One outstanding puzzle is "What causes the pronounced increase in breathing during exercise?" As a first guess you might say something like this: "During exercise muscles use more O_2 and produce more CO_2. This results in a low blood O_2 concentration, and high CO_2 concentration; and, as we know, both of these factors increase breathing." Logical as this seems, it is not the whole answer. During severe exercise, the extent of the increase in breathing is so great that the level of CO_2 and O_2 in the blood may not show *any* substantial change! This large increase in breathing could not be produced by the simple responses to low O_2 and high CO_2 that we have outlined. Something else *must* be involved, but what? It remains to be discovered.

During the act of breathing, water is lost from the body. It

Wide World Photos

Fig. 7.10 This runner is breathing hard. Why? The physiological causes are not yet fully understood.

simply evaporates from the moist surfaces of the lungs and is expelled with each breath. The amount of water lost in this way has no relation to the needs of the body for water, but occurs incidentally with the body's exchange of O_2 and CO_2 with the external environment. Water is also lost through the skin (for example, by sweating), the intestinal tract, and the kidney. Of these various routes for water loss, only the kidney responds to the body's needs for water and acts to regulate it. In the next chapter we shall turn our attention to the role of the kidney in the regulation of salt and water.

SUMMARY

Oxygen enters the body through the lungs, is picked up by **hemoglobin** in the red blood cells, and is carried to the body tissues where it is used. The carbon dioxide produced by the tissues is carried (as bicarbonate, or in combination with hemoglobin) by the blood back to the lungs, where it is eliminated. Hemoglobin also helps stabilize the concentration of hydrogen ions in the blood.

The amount of hemoglobin contained in the blood is regulated by the production of red blood cells. The rate of red cell production depends on the oxygen content of the blood. Whenever the oxygen content is low, the rate of production of red cells increases. This slowly increases the hemoglobin concentration and compensates for the original reduction in oxygen content.

Faster responses are brought about by the regulation of breathing. Breathing is increased whenever the level of oxygen in the blood is lowered, or whenever the carbon dioxide level is raised. **Chemoreceptors,** which are sensitive to the reduced level of oxygen, respond by sending impulses to the respiratory centers, which in turn stimulate breathing. This compensates for the original oxygen deficit. Excess carbon dioxide acts directly on the brain; the respiratory centers again respond and breathing is increased. This compensates for the original carbon dioxide excess. Normally, the response to an excess of carbon dioxide is much stronger than the response to a deficit in oxygen.

FOR THOUGHT AND DISCUSSION

1 The term *hypoxia* usually refers to a condition in which the availability or utilization of oxygen is depressed. The data listed below illustrate four different types of hypoxia compared with the state of a "normal" person breathing fresh room air. (The weight, sex, and age of all subjects are the same.)

Subject	Hemoglobin (grams Hb per 100 ml blood)	O₂ content of arterial blood (ml O₂ per 100 ml blood)	O₂ content of venous blood (ml O₂ per 100 ml blood)	Cardiac output (liters/ min)
A NORMAL	15	19	15	5.0
B HYPOXIA	15	15	12	6.6
C HYPOXIA	8	9.5	6.5	7.0
D HYPOXIA	16	20	13	3.0
E HYPOXIA	15	19	18	no information

(a) Which subject is suffering from a dietary iron deficiency?

(b) Which subject is suffering from heart failure and poor blood circulation?

(c) Which subject has recently climbed a mountain, where the air is "thin" and atmospheric oxygen low?

(d) Which subject is suffering from a poison (for example, cyanide) which prevents his cells from using oxygen?

(e) Breathing has increased in subject B. Briefly describe the physiological mechanism that is responsible.

(f) In subject A how much blood is flowing through the lungs each minute? Using this figure, and data from the table, calculate how many cc of oxygen are carried *to* the lungs each minute. How many cc of oxygen are carried *away* from the lungs each minute. Using these last two figures, calculate the oxygen consumed each minute.

(g) A standard method of measuring cardiac output is to measure oxygen consumption during each minute along with the oxygen content of both the arterial and venous blood. Cardiac output is calculated from these figures. Explain. [HINT: study your answer to question 1(f).]

2 A large blood vessel is cut and the bleeding is severe. Outline the physiological responses (discussed in this and the preceding two chapters) that will help the person to survive.

SELECTED READINGS

Carlson, A. J., V. Johnson, and H. M. Cavert. *The Machinery of the Body,* 5th Ed. Chicago: University of Chicago Press, 1961.

Chapman, C. B. and J. H. Mitchell. "The Physiology of Exercise," *Scientific American* (May 1965) (*Scientific American* reprint #1011).

Comroe, J. H. "The Lung," *Scientific American* (February 1966).

———. *Physiology of Respiration.* Chicago: Yearbook Medical Publishers, Inc., 1965.

McDermott, W. "Air Pollution and Public Health," *Scientific American* (October 1961) (*Scientific American* reprint #612).

8 SALT AND WATER: THE KIDNEY

At that time in the long course of evolution when animals first left fresh water and began to spread over the land, they were faced with a new danger—the threat of drying up. In order to survive on the land, they had to develop a way of conserving water. Man still faces this threat. The living cells making up your body must be bathed in a watery fluid to survive. The regulation of the salt and water content of this fluid is largely the responsibility of the kidney. If we drink too little water, the kidney excretes less water in the urine. If we drink too much, the kidney excretes more water in the urine.

The work of the kidney, however, is not limited to the regulation of salt and water alone. It also plays a very important role in the regulation of the acidity of the blood, and in the excretion of waste products. The waste product **urea,** for example, which is formed when proteins are broken down, is eliminated from the body primarily by the kidney.

Wide World Photos

Fig. 8.1 The living cells of your body must be bathed in a watery solution if they are to survive. Although this man is surrounded by sea water, he must find other water to drink.

Structure of the Kidney

In Fig. 8.2 we see the two kidneys as they rest in the abdominal cavity. Three important tubes are attached: 1. The **renal artery,** which conducts blood from the aorta to the kidney. 2. The **renal vein,** which conducts blood away from the kidney. 3. A **ureter** from each kidney conducting urine from the kidneys to the bladder. Somehow, the kidneys are able to extract materials from the blood that passes through them, and then pass these materials into the ureter, where we identify them as components of urine.

If we use a microscope to take a closer look, we find that each kidney contains about a million tiny tubes, called **nephrons.** These tubes are the actual site of urine formation. A nephron is a long structure with walls composed of a single layer of cells. One end of the nephron is enlarged into a funnel-like structure called the **capsule.** The other end of this tube empties into a larger tube called the **collecting duct** (see Fig. 8.3).

Blood comes in contact with the nephrons by means of two capillary beds arranged in series. The first capillary bed, called the **glomerulus,** is contained within the funnel-like structure of the capsule, and is shown in detail in Fig. 8.4. Blood leaving the glomerulus does not return directly to the larger veins, as we would normally expect. Rather, it flows out through the **efferent arteriole** and enters another capillary bed, which supplies the cells lining the tubules (Fig. 8.3).

The Formation of Urine

The formation of urine from blood takes place in two major steps. First, the blood cells and plasma proteins are separated from a portion of blood. Second, the composition of this portion is changed until it becomes urine. Let us trace the details of these two steps with the aid of Fig. 8.4. Blood enters the kidney from the renal artery and finds its way to the glomerular capillaries. Here, one-fifth of the plasma *filters* through the capillary walls and is collected in the funnel-like structure. The other four-fifths continues on toward the tubule capillaries. The pores in the glomerular walls are too small to permit large protein molecules or cells to pass through them. The fluid that filters through is like plasma, except that it does not contain protein or cells.

The filtered fluid flows from the capsule into the tubule and on toward the collecting ducts and finally into the ureter. Fluid entering the tubule is very much like plasma. Fluid leaving the tubule resembles urine. It follows that the composition of the

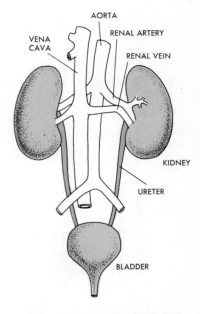

Fig. 8.2 The kidneys form urine by extracting material from the blood passing through them.

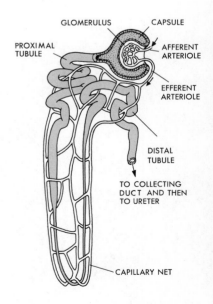

Fig. 8.3 The *nephron* shown in color is the functional unit of the kidney.

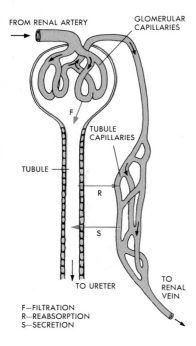

FROM RENAL ARTERY   GLOMERULAR CAPILLARIES

TUBULE CAPILLARIES

F

TUBULE

R

S

TO URETER

TO RENAL VEIN

F—FILTRATION
R—REABSORPTION
S—SECRETION

Fig. 8.4 Urine formation takes place in two stages. First, water and small molecules filter through the *glomerulus* into the tubules; second, the composition of filtered fluid is changed by tubular *reabsorption* and *secretion*.

fluid changes as it flows down the tubule. Many substances are transported from the tubular fluid through the cells of the tubular walls and redeposited into the blood capillaries that supply these cells. This process is called **reabsorption.** A few substances are transported in the reverse direction—from the blood to the tubular fluid. This is called **tubular secretion.**

The process of urine formation, then, takes place in two steps. 1. *Filtration* in the glomerulus involves a large volume of fluid which is filtered from the blood and sent into the tubules. Proteins and blood cells are held back and, consequently, never appear in the urine. 2. *Reabsorption and tubular secretion* in the tubules is the second step. Cells lining the tubular walls transport materials either from the tubules to the blood (reabsorption) or from the blood to the tubules (tubular secretion). The altered fluid reaching the end of the collecting duct enters the ureter as urine.

Evidence for filtration: We have uncovered several facts that make us believe that filtration is the first step in urine formation. 1. Large molecules are never found in normal urine. Evidently, they cannot pass through the filter. 2. Pressure must be relatively high to force fluids through a filter. If blood pressure dropped sufficiently, we would expect the glomerular filter to stop working. This seems to happen. When the arterial blood pressure falls below 70 mm Hg, urine formation stops. 3. Samples of fluid have been taken from the capsule and chemically analyzed. The chemical composition of the capsule fluid is identical to that of the plasma, with the exception that the fluid does not contain proteins. This is just what we would expect in a filtration process.

Mechanisms of reabsorption: Reabsorption is a key process in urine formation. As an example, consider the reabsorption of water. During each minute, a normal person has roughly 600 ml of plasma flowing through his kidneys. Of this 600 ml, one-fifth, or 120 ml, is filtered. On the other hand, under average conditions only about 1 ml of urine is formed per minute. In other words, during each minute 120 ml of fluid enter the tubules through the filtration process but only 1 ml of fluid leaves. This means that more than 99 per cent of the fluid (which is mostly water) is reabsorbed. These figures are surprisingly large. There are only about 3000 ml of plasma in the entire body. In about 25 minutes a volume of fluid equivalent to the entire plasma volume filters through the glomerulus. In other words, the kidney samples the entire plasma volume about every 25 minutes! Imagine what would happen if the reabsorption mechanism failed. We would simply excrete our body fluids into the urine and the whole living system would collapse.

What is responsible for the reabsorption of such a large volume of fluid? Experiments indicate that the prime mover in reabsorption of fluid is the active transport of sodium from the tubular fluid to the blood. Sodium is one of the most abundant solutes in the plasma. As fluid progresses down the tubules, sodium is pumped back into the blood by the cells lining the walls of the tubule. As we saw earlier, sodium contains a net-positive charge, so it attracts negatively charged particles. Each time a sodium ion is pumped out of the tubule, it upsets the charge balance. As a result a negatively charged particle will follow it. Usually, this is chloride, since it is the most abundant negatively charged ion in the tubular fluid. In other words, salt (sodium chloride) moves from the tubular fluid back into the plasma.

The water movements that take place during this process can be explained by the osmotic pressure of the tubular fluid, which decreases each time a solute molecule is reabsorbed. As a result, water is drawn out to balance the osmotic pressure. It follows the movement of sodium chloride. Thus, simply by pumping sodium out of the tubule, both chloride and water are reabsorbed into the blood plasma. In fact, the major portion of water that is reabsorbed is due to the initial pumping of sodium. The reabsorption of water influences other solutes in the tubules. This is because whenever water leaves the tubular fluids, any solutes that remain behind become more concentrated. If these solutes can pass through the tubular walls, they may simply diffuse back into the blood.

Sodium is not the only substance that is actively transported in the reabsorption process. Glucose and amino acids, for example, are pumped from the tubular fluid back into the blood. Ordinarily, all of the glucose is transported in this way; none appears in the urine. However, in some rare cases the blood may contain so much glucose that when it is filtered into the tubules the walls become overloaded. The transport system cannot handle all of the glucose that comes to it. Some of the glucose remains behind in the tubular fluids and eventually finds its way into the urine.

In summary, the reabsorption of huge amounts of water during each minute occurs by simple osmosis. The osmotic forces responsible for this are a direct result of the reabsorption of sodium chloride. This withdrawal (by reabsorption) of water from the tubules concentrates any solutes left behind. Any of these concentrated solutes which cannot penetrate the tubular walls easily will be found in high concentrations in the urine. This is true of some waste products. Any solute that can penetrate the tubular walls will be reabsorbed to a certain extent

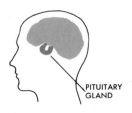

PITUITARY
GLAND

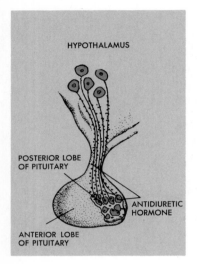

HYPOTHALAMUS

POSTERIOR LOBE
OF PITUITARY

ANTIDIURETIC
HORMONE

ANTERIOR LOBE
OF PITUITARY

Fig. 8.5 ADH is made in the *hypothalamus* and migrates to the *pituitary* gland, where it may be stored, or released into the blood.

because it will simply diffuse from tubular fluid (where the solute is concentrated) to blood. Finally, we emphasize that many important solutes like sodium, glucose, and amino acids are reabsorbed by an active process requiring energy supplied by the metabolism of the tubular cells.

Regulating Osmotic Pressure in Body Fluids

The body gains and loses water and salts in a variety of ways. As you found in the last chapter, some body water is lost with each breath, but the rate of breathing (which depends on blood carbon dioxide and oxygen concentrations) is not governed by the body's needs for water. We also lose water through sweating, but this is also not regulated by the body's water requirements. Nevertheless, in spite of large variations in water loss by these two routes, the changes in osmotic pressure of the body fluids are very small. This is because the kidney *is* responsive to the body's water requirements. By altering the amount of water excreted in the urine, the kidney regulates the osmotic pressure.

A simple example will demonstrate how accurately the kidney works. If you drink a quart of water quickly you find that you produce much more urine than normal over the next three or four hours. If you collect the excess urine during this period, you find that there is just about a quart of it. But after three or four hours, urine production returns to normal. Somehow or other, the kidney "knew" just how much extra water you drank. It excreted almost precisely that amount so that the body's water content would remain constant. How does the kidney "know" when to excrete extra water and when to conserve it? What are the details of this homeostatic response?

A hormone called **antidiuretic hormone** (**ADH**) plays a central role in the regulation of body water. It acts directly on the kidney tubules causing an increase in water reabsorption. When the body's water supply is low, a large amount of ADH is present in the blood. This causes the kidney to conserve water because most of the tubular water is reabsorbed and cannot pass into the urine. The output of urine may be as little as $1/2$ ml per minute at this time.

When the body contains excessive water, very little ADH is present in the blood, so the capacity of the kidney to reabsorb water is reduced. Some of the tubular water that normally would have been reabsorbed now passes into the urine. Urine output may rise to 16 ml per minute. How does ADH increase in the blood when we need to conserve water? Where does the ADH come from?

ADH is manufactured by specialized nerve cells lying in the

hypothalamus—a small region at the base of the brain. These cells send fibers a very short distance to the posterior **pituitary** gland (Fig. 8.5). ADH produced by these cells migrates along the fibers to the pituitary gland where it may be stored or released into the blood stream. The release of this hormone is controlled to a large extent by specialized nerve cells called **osmoreceptors** (located in the hypothalamus), which are sensitive to the osmotic pressure of the fluids that surround them. When the body has too little water, the osmotic pressure of the fluids goes up. The osmoreceptors respond and the rate of release of ADH is increased. As a result, more water is reabsorbed by the kidney. When too much fluid is taken in, the osmotic pressure of body fluids goes down. Less ADH is released by the gland, and more water passes into the urine. This homeostatic feedback system is shown in Fig. 8.6.

Many experiments support the scheme that we have outlined above. In one of the most dramatic tests, an animal's pituitary glands may be removed, which means that there is no longer a source of ADH. Urine flow increases dangerously because the tubules can no longer reabsorb a normal amount of water. If we now prepare an extract of the gland and inject it into the animal, the urine flow returns to normal. Apparently the extract of the gland contains enough ADH to restore the ability of the tubules to reabsorb water. This same dramatic increase in urine flow occurs in humans when the back (posterior) part of the pituitary gland is damaged.

What does ADH do to the tubules to allow them to reabsorb more water? Before we can pursue this question, we will need more information about the structure of the nephron (Fig. 8.7).

Fig. 8.6 ADH, released when the osmotic pressure of the blood plasma increases, acts on the kidney by promoting an increase in water reabsorption. The feedback loop shows how this response helps stabilize the osmotic pressure of the body fluids.

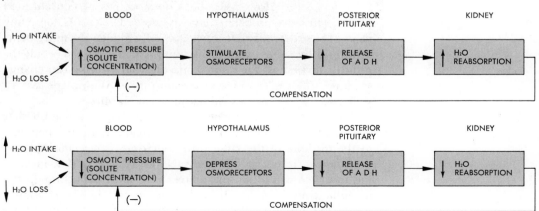

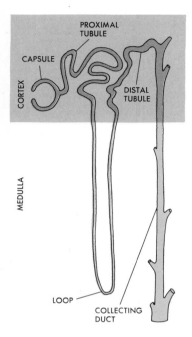

Fig. 8.7 The nephron consists of three main parts— the *proximal tubule,* the *loop,* and the *distal tubule.*

Structure of the Nephron

For convenience, we divide the tubule into three parts. 1. That part of the tubule that is attached to the funnel-like capsule is called the **proximal tubule.** It lies almost entirely in the surface layers, or **cortex** (cortex means bark), of the kidney. 2. The second portion of the tubule is called the **loop.** It takes a straight course and dips deeply into the core (or **medulla**) of the kidney. Then it bends back out toward the cortex. 3. When the tubule re-enters the cortex it becomes the **distal tubule.** The distal tubule enters into the collecting duct, which again proceeds downward into the core of the kidney.

Under most circumstances the proximal tubule does the same job. It reabsorbs about 85 per cent of the water that has been filtered in the glomerulus. In addition, it reabsorbs all of the glucose, and a large number of other substances, such as amino acids and vitamins, which are essential to the internal environment. The remaining 15 per cent of the fluid passes down through the loop and on toward the distal tubule and the collecting ducts. By varying the reabsorption of the last 15 per cent of the water, the kidney regulates the fluid volume of the internal environment.

When we study the role of the kidney in water regulation, we must not lose sight of the fact that the kidney always excretes some solutes. For example, it excretes waste products like urea whether it is conserving or excreting water. When excess water is excreted it is as though the excess water were added to the load of waste products normally excreted, thus making the urine very dilute. On the other hand, when water is conserved, the urine is highly concentrated.

Mechanism of Action of ADH

How does the kidney excrete a concentrated urine? This is a problem that has puzzled scientists for many years. They reasoned that water normally follows the movements of solutes by simple osmosis. If this were the case, it would be difficult to see how the solute concentration of urine can change so drastically under different circumstances. Within the last 10 years, the answer to this riddle has been clarified.

The most important clue was the startling observation that solutes contained in the tissue spaces surrounding the nephron in the medulla of the kidney are four times more concentrated than anywhere else in the body. Notice (Fig. 8.7) that in passing from the capsule to the ureter, fluid must pass through the medulla twice, first in the loop and second in the collecting ducts. The first time through, sodium is pumped out of the as-

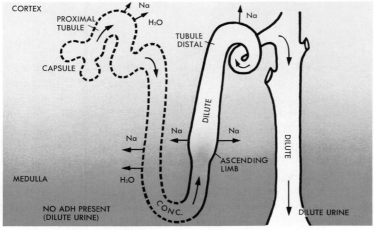

Drawn after Best and Taylor, The Physiological Basis of Medical Practice, 7 ed., Williams & Wilkins

Fig. 8.8 If ADH secretion stops or is low, the urine will be dilute because the walls of the distal tubule and collecting duct are impermeable to water. (Broken lines represent water permeable walls of the nephron; solid lines represent water impermeable walls.)

cending limb of the loop, but water cannot follow it because the tubular walls of this segment of the loop are impermeable to water. Sodium collects in the extracellular spaces of the medulla, accounting for the fact that it is four times more concentrated than other body fluids.

The loop of the nephron has loaded the spaces with solute in preparation for the second passage through the medulla. Since sodium has been removed from the loop, the fluid presented to the distal tubule will be dilute. The fate of the tubular fluid from this point onward depends on whether or not the hormone ADH is present. If there is little or no ADH, the remaining parts of the nephron—from distal tubule through the collecting duct—are impermeable to water. Although some solute may be reabsorbed from the fluid in these parts, water is not. This makes the fluid more dilute (by losing solute) and the result is very dilute urine (Fig. 8.8).

However, if much ADH is present, it acts in some unknown

Best and Taylor

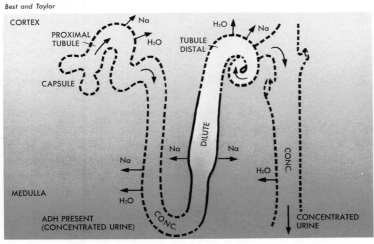

Fig. 8.9 If there is an abundant supply of ADH, the urine will be concentrated because ADH makes the walls of the distal tubules and collecting ducts permeable to water. (Broken lines represent water permeable walls of the nephron; solid lines represent water impermeable walls.)

manner on the distal tubule and collecting duct, making them permeable to water. As a result, water leaves the distal tubule and collecting duct by osmosis (Fig. 8.9). But we have just seen that the collecting ducts must pass through the medulla. Because solutes are highly concentrated in the medulla, water will leave the ducts until fluid within the ducts is just as concentrated as the outside fluid. In short, when a large quantity of ADH is present, the urine will be concentrated.

The transfer of water in the kidney is a passive process. Water flows from regions of low osmotic pressure to regions of higher osmotic pressure. It is completely controlled by the solute distribution. But the kidney can pump sodium, and water will follow the sodium. So, by pumping sodium the kidney can regulate the water content of urine. This also regulates the water content of the body. When sodium is pumped into the medulla, the fluid in the extracellular spaces become concentrated. The fluid in the collecting duct and, therefore, the urine never gets more concentrated than the fluid in the medullary extracellular spaces.

This limitation on the concentration of solutes in the urine explains why it is not wise to drink sea water when you are thirsty. The concentration of salt in sea water is usually larger than the highest concentration of the salt that the kidney can excrete. The effect of drinking sea water, then, is to increase the solute content of the body fluids, and it is this increased solute content which created the original need for water. This will increase your thirst. Instead of alleviating the problem you only aggravate it by drinking sea water. You have set the *positive feedback* loop illustrated in Fig. 8.10 into operation. If you continue to drink sea water, the increase in body salt content will become a threat to survival.

Fig. 8.10 The ability of the kidney to excrete a high concentration of salt in the urine is limited. Drinking salt water that is even more concentrated can only increase the concentration of solutes in the body fluids. This initiates sensations of thirst which may set the *positive* feedback loop shown here into operation.

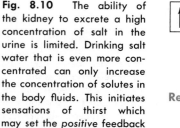
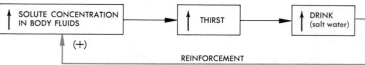

Regulation of Body Fluid Volume

We have seen that the pituitary gland and kidney interact and regulate the *concentration* of solutes. The kidney also interacts with another gland, the adrenal cortex (Fig. 10.6) to control the *amount* or *volume* of the body fluids. The adrenal gland secretes many hormones. One of them called **aldosterone** may be involved in regulation of body fluid volume. It acts on

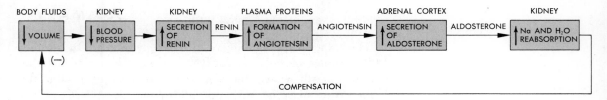

BODY FLUIDS   KIDNEY   KIDNEY   PLASMA PROTEINS   ADRENAL CORTEX   KIDNEY

↓ VOLUME → ↓ BLOOD PRESSURE → ↑ SECRETION OF RENIN → RENIN → ↑ FORMATION OF ANGIOTENSIN → ANGIOTENSIN → ↑ SECRETION OF ALDOSTERONE → ALDOSTERONE → ↑ Na AND H₂O REABSORPTION

↑ (−)

COMPENSATION

kidney tubules by increasing the reabsorption of sodium. The more the tubules reabsorb sodium, the more water they will reabsorb to maintain an osmotic balance. In other words, the secretion of aldosterone acts to conserve body fluids. It is secreted when the volume of body fluids drops. This probably occurs in the following way (see Fig. 8.11): a reduction in body fluid volume is usually accompanied by a reduction in blood volume. A reduction in blood volume, in turn, may be accompanied by a reduction in blood pressure in the kidneys. The kidneys respond to this lowered blood pressure by releasing a substance called **renin** into the blood. Renin acts on one of the plasma proteins and produces a new substance called **angiotensin.** Finally, angiotensin stimulates the release of aldosterone by the adrenal gland. The details of this complicated feedback loop are illustrated in Fig. 8.11.

Fig. 8.11 When the body fluid volume is decreased, the secretion of aldosterone is increased. Aldosterone stimulates an increase in sodium (and water) reabsorption by the kidney. This response helps compensate for the decrease in body fluid volume. Recent experiments suggest that the feedback loop shown above is involved in stabilizing the volume of body fluids.

Other Functions of the Kidney

Besides regulating salt and water, the kidney helps regulate the acidity of the blood. This process occurs in the distal tubules, where the cells are able to actively transport H^+ from the blood to the tubular fluid and thus dispose of excess acid.

The role of the kidney in excreting waste products is an extremely important one. Some wastes are simply filtered through the glomerulus and are not reabsorbed as rapidly as water. They are thus more concentrated in the urine than in the blood. As a result, there is a net loss of these materials from the body. Urea, which is produced in the liver from waste products of protein breakdown, is a good example of this type of excretion. Other substances are more actively removed. In addition to being filtered through the glomerulus, they are transported from the blood to the tubular fluid (the exact opposite of reabsorption) by the tubular cells.

In this chapter we have been concerned with homeostatic mechanisms that operate on the outflow of materials from the internal environment. In the next chapter we turn our attention to the gastro-intestinal tract, a major avenue for the inflow of materials into the internal environment.

SUMMARY

The kidney helps regulate the internal environment by forming and excreting urine. Urine contains waste products and variable amounts of salt, water, and acid. The formation of urine in the kidney takes place in two stages—**filtration,** then selective **reabsorption** (or the opposite, **secretion**).

The kidney is responsible for regulating the osmotic pressure of the body fluids. When the osmotic pressure of the blood reaching the hypothalamus is increased, special cells (osmoreceptors) respond and the hormone ADH is released in greater quantities by the **posterior pituitary gland.** ADH acts on the kidney and causes an increase in the reabsorption of water; the body fluids are then diluted back toward normal.

The action of ADH: the fluids surrounding the nephrons in the medulla are very highly concentrated because of the active transport of sodium. In the presence of ADH, the walls of the collecting duct and distal tubules become permeable to water, fluid is reabsorbed (by osmosis) in large quantities from the collecting duct into the medulla; the urine becomes concentrated. In the absence of ADH, the walls of the collecting ducts and distal tubules are relatively impermeable to water. Fluid reabsorption is diminished and large quantities of water are excreted in the urine.

The reabsorption of sodium by the kidneys is controlled in part by a hormone called *aldosterone.* Aldosterone acts on the kidney tubules and increases the reabsorption of sodium. The more the tubules reabsorb sodium, the more water they will reabsorb, thus maintaining an osmotic balance. In this way, aldosterone is involved in the control of the volume of body fluids.

FOR THOUGHT AND DISCUSSION

1 Trace the possible routes taken by a glucose molecule as it enters the kidney through the renal artery. How do these routes differ from the route taken by a urea molecule that finds its way into the urine?

2 In some abnormal cases, the blood may contain so much glucose that when it is filtered into the nephron the tubules are not able to reabsorb all of it, and some glucose appears in the urine. In these cases, the volume of water excreted in the urine may be abnormally high. Explain.

3 In some cases of kidney disease, the glomerular membrane becomes very much more permeable than it is normally. The

body tissues of patients (who have the disease) usually swell and become distended with fluid (*edema*). Can you suggest an explanation? (HINT: what substance normally excluded from the urine by the filtration process may now find its way through the highly permeable glomerular membrane?)

4 A man is lost in the desert without any water supply. What physiological responses described in this chapter will tend to help him survive?

SELECTED READINGS

Best, C. H. and N. B. Taylor. *The Physiological Basis of Medical Practice,* 7th Ed. Baltimore: Williams and Wilkins, 1961.

Carlson, A. J., V. Johnson, and H. M. Cavert. *The Machinery of the Body,* 5th Ed. Chicago: University of Chicago Press, 1961.

Merrill, J. P. "The Artificial Kidney," *Scientific American* (July 1961).

Pitts, R. F., *Physiology of the Kidney and Body Fluids.* Chicago: Yearbook Medical Publishers, 1963.

Schmidt-Nielsen, K. and B. Schmidt-Nielsen. "The Desert Rat," *Scientific American* (July 1953).

Smith, H. W. *From Fish to Philosopher.* Boston: Little, Brown, and Co., 1953.

Solomon, A. K. "Pumps in the Living Cell," *Scientific American* (August 1962).

Wolf, A. V. "Thirst," *Scientific American* (January 1956).

9 FOOD

When cellular life began on the Earth, every cell was in direct contact with the sea. From this liquid environment the cell was able to obtain all of its nutritional requirements. As animal life became more complex, tissues and organs developed. Because the cells of certain tissues and organs were neither on the surface of the body nor in direct contact with the sea, the cells had to be supplied with food from the external environment in a new way. The evolution of the **gastro-intestinal tract** helped satisfy this requirement.

The gastro-intestinal tract (GI tract) is a long, hollow tube lying deep within the body. Both ends of this tube open onto the surface of the body (Fig. 9.2). The digestive system is made up of the various organs shown in Fig. 9.3: the **mouth** (including teeth and salivary glands), the **esophagus,** which conveys food to the **stomach** where it is stored and mixed, the **small intestine** into which the liver and the pancreas secrete materials, and the **large intestine** with its terminal opening, the **anus.** The

Fig. 9.1 Breugel's painting "The Peasant Wedding."

GI tract, which is about 15 feet long in the living body, is contained within a body (head and trunk) only about four feet long. As a result, the GI tract is folded over on itself many times. You can see from both Figs. 9.2 and 9.3 that swallowed food within the GI tract is still *outside* of the internal environment. To enter the internal environment, it must be transported across the cellular walls of the GI tract and into the bloodstream. The process by which this transport occurs is called **absorption.**

Only certain types of molecules are absorbed by the cellular walls of the GI tract. This is an advantage because our diet may contain many things that would be harmful if they entered the blood. Most of the foods that we eat are complex molecules which must be broken down into simpler building blocks before they can be absorbed. This breakdown process is called **digestion.** In this chapter, we investigate the nature of the foods we eat. We also ask how they are broken down by the processes of digestion, how the simpler products of digestion are absorbed, and how these various processes are controlled.

FOOD AND DIGESTION

The foods we normally eat fall into one of the following categories: carbohydrates, fats, proteins, minerals, vitamins, or water. Vitamins, minerals, and water do not have to be digested in order to be absorbed. Other compounds, such as cellulose (a plant carbohydrate) pass right through the human GI tract without being absorbed, since there are no enzymes for digesting these compounds into simpler building blocks. Carbohydrates, fats, and proteins are complicated molecules and must be broken down into simpler molecules if they are to be absorbed.

The breakdown of food into simple molecules occurs because the inner walls of the GI tract, and certain large glands associated with the tract, are able to secrete enzymes. Enzymes act as **catalysts**—they increase the rate of chemical reactions but they do not influence the direction of those reactions. They seem to work by providing a surface upon which the reaction may take place easily. Enzymes are *specific* in their action; that is, a particular enzyme is required for a particular reaction. The various digestive enzymes can be classed according to the basic foods upon which they work.

Classes of Food

Carbohydrates: The class of food called carbohydrates includes the sugars and the starches. These compounds

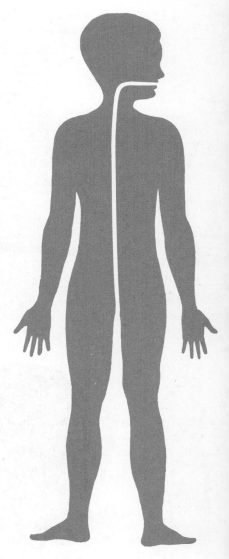

Fig. 9.2 The gastro-intestinal tract is a hollow tube, both ends of which open to the external environment. Actually the GI tract is part of the body's surface. Even though food is within the GI tract, it is outside of the internal environment.

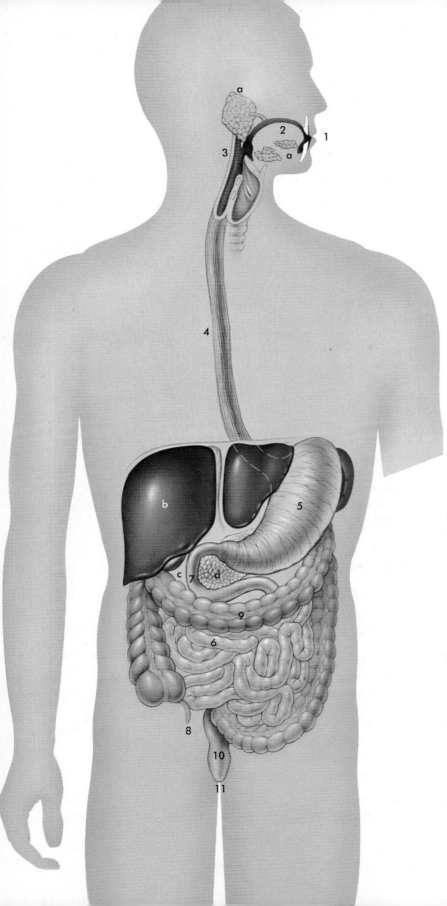

GASTRO-INTESTINAL TRACT

1 MOUTH

2 TONGUE

3 PHARYNX

4 ESOPHAGUS

5 STOMACH

6 SMALL INTESTINE

7 DUODENUM

8 APPENDIX

9 LARGE INTESTINE

10 RECTUM

11 ANUS

ASSOCIATED STRUCTURES

a SALIVARY GLANDS

b LIVER

c GALLBLADDER

d PANCREAS

THE DIGESTIVE SYSTEM

Fig. 9.3 The gastro-intestinal tract is a specialized surface of the body. When food enters the GI tract it is chewed, then mixed, and lubricated by salivary secretions. Swallowing carries it to the stomach, where digestive secretions begin to attack the proteins, but the food is not yet ready for absorption by the blood stream. When moved into the small intestine the food is subjected to the action of new secretions (from the liver, pancreas, and small intestine walls) that complete the job of digestion. It is in the small intestine that absorption into the blood stream takes place. Food that has not been absorbed is moved into the large intestine. Waste is finally eliminated through the anus.

TABLE 9.1

Food	*Products: Building Blocks Which Can Be Absorbed*
Fat (Lipid) ⟶	Glycerol, Fatty Acids,
Carbohydrates ⟶	Simple Sugars,
Proteins ⟶	Amino Acids

all contain carbon, hydrogen, and oxygen. Usually there are two hydrogen atoms for every oxygen atom. The building blocks of the common carbohydrates in our food are the simple, single sugars which contain six carbon atoms $C_6H_{12}O_6$. Two simple sugars can be joined by a chemical bond, forming a double sugar. In the process two atoms of hydrogen and one atom of oxygen are removed, so that the formula of a double sugar is $C_{12}H_{22}O_{11}$. Common table sugar (**sucrose**) is a double sugar. The sugar of the blood (**glucose**) is a simple six-carbon sugar.

Proteins: These are extremely large compounds made up of anywhere from about 100 to many thousands of smaller building blocks called **amino acids.** There are only about 20 different kinds of amino acids commonly found in proteins; but like the letters of the alphabet, they can be joined together in an endless variety of combinations and sequences, thus forming different protein molecules.

Amino acids are the constituents of protein that are absorbed by the digestive system. The proteins we eat must be broken down by a class of enzymes called **proteases** into amino acids. Of the 20 different amino acids, eight are termed **essential** because they cannot be formed by the body and, therefore, must be included in the proteins we eat. The remaining 12 amino acids can be formed from other substances in the body.

Once the amino acids are absorbed, they can be assembled into many new kinds of proteins by the cells of the body. However, the sequence in which the amino acids are joined to form some of these proteins is different for each cell type. Some of the proteins found in muscle cells, for example, differ from those found in kidney cells. When you eat beef, you swallow cattle-protein, but the beef protein never enters your blood. Instead, it is first broken down (digested) into its component amino acids; the amino acids are then absorbed into the blood, and finally new protein is constructed from these amino acids. This new protein is used in many different ways—for example, in the formation of enzymes, and in the formation of various cellular structures. Some of the proteins that your body builds are different from those of any other person! This is one of the things that make you different from every other person in the world.

Fats: These substances are made up of any three of the many different fatty acids chemically bonded to one glycerol molecule. Fats must also be broken down into simpler units in order to be absorbed. The lipases form the general class of enzymes responsible for this breakdown.

TABLE 9.2   Chemical Factors in Digestion

Gland	Secretes	Digestive Juice Acts Upon	Digestion Products
Salivary	Salivary amylase (ptyalin)	Cooked Starch	Double sugar
Stomach (gastric glands in stomach walls)	HCl** and pepsin (protease)	Proteins	Intermediate stages between proteins and amino acids
Liver	Bile salts**	Large fat droplets	Emulsified fat (small droplets)
Pancreas	Pancreatic amylase	Intact or partially digested starches	Double sugar
	Trypsin*** (protease)	Intact or partially digested proteins	Small amino acid groups (peptides)
	Steapsin (Lipase)	Fats	**Fatty acids†** **glycerol†**
Small intestine (glands in intestinal wall)	Erepsin (peptidase)	Split products of gastric and pancreatic digestion of proteins	**Amino acids†**
	(Enterokinase)	(Inactive trypsinogen)	(Active trypsin)
	Several carbohydrate-splitting enzymes	Double sugars	**Simple sugar†**

** Not enzymes
*** Secreted as inactive trypsinogen, which is converted to active trypsin by enterokinase
† In a state which can be absorbed

Adapted from *The Machinery of The Body*, by Carlson, Johnson, and Cavert

Enzymes: Table 9.2 shows a list of enzymes which are released into the GI tract and act upon the various foods we eat. You might wonder why the digestive enzymes do not attack and digest the walls of the stomach and the intestines themselves. The proteins that make up the structural components of the GI tract walls are protected by a coating of mucous which also lubricates the GI tract. But this is not the whole answer. Somewhere the digestive enzymes have to be formed. If they are formed in cells, then why don't they digest each cell that forms them? One possible explanation is that some enzymes are not present in an *active* form inside the cell. They are converted into an active form only after they have been secreted into the GI tract. Thus, the stomach enzyme **pepsin** is secreted in an inactive form known as **pepsinogen.** Pepsinogen is converted to an active form by the hydrochloric acid which is secreted in other parts of the stomach. Similarly, the enzyme **trypsin,** which comes from the pancreas, is secreted in an inactive form called **trypsinogen.** Trypsinogen is converted to the active trypsin by another enzyme, one which is liberated by the intestinal walls.

The enzymes listed in Table 9.2 are not secreted continuously into the gastro-intestinal tract. They are secreted in a more economical way only when food is present. Some are secreted only when specific types of food are present. Even though secretion is not continuous, on the average a person secretes four to nine liters of fluid into the GI tract each day!

Control of Digestive Secretions

Digestive enzymes and fluids are usually secreted in response to foods in the GI tract. The foods act by 1. stimulating sensory nerve endings which are involved in reflex control of secretion; 2. causing the release of hormones which in turn act on the secreting cells of the GI tract; and 3. simple mechanical stimulation of the walls of the tract. In the mouth, secretion of saliva is primarily under the control of nerve reflexes, but further down the tract, in the stomach and intestines, secretion is controlled by all three mechanisms—nerve reflex, hormonal, and mechanical stimulation.

A study of digestion in the stomach offers a good example of how the various types of control mechanisms have been discovered. The cells of the stomach secrete pepsin (which digests proteins), hydrochloric acid (which activates pepsin), and mucous.

The different types of control are most dramatically seen in animals which have had their gastro-intestinal tract surgically altered. Fig. 9.4 shows an experimental animal whose esophagus has been severed and the top portion sewn to the outside of its

Fig. 9.4 When food is placed in the mouth, gastric juices are secreted in the stomach. If the vagus nerves are cut, this response is lost, demonstrating *neural control* of gastric secretion.

body. When the animal eats, the food never enters the stomach, it just drops back into the dish. The lower cut end of the esophagus is also sewn to the outside, enabling the animal to be fed artificially. Finally, part of the stomach is opened to the outside so that its contents can be examined.

This animal can be used to demonstrate that the stomach is under nervous control before food enters it. For example, when the animal eats, gastric juices (enzymes, HCl) drip into the funnel from the stomach even though food never reaches the stomach. This same response, a nervous response, results from the sight, smell, or taste of food. The response produces one-half of the gastric juice that is secreted during a meal. When the two vagus nerves (the nerves of the stomach and most of the digestive system) are cut, this response is lost.

Even when all of the nerves of the stomach are cut, gastric juice is still released when food enters the stomach. This response, which is independent of the nervous system, seems to be controlled by at least two things: 1. when food enters the stomach and is churned and mixed there, the cells that secrete gastric juice are stimulated by the churning action. 2. There is also evidence that a hormone called **gastrin** is liberated when the stomach contains partially digested proteins. Gastrin, being a hormone, is not liberated into the stomach, but into the blood stream and is carried by the blood to the cells which produce gastric juice. We can show this hormonal effect by transplanting a piece of stomach to the skin (Fig. 9.5). When proteins enter the intact stomach the small piece of transplanted stomach begins to produce a gastric juice. Since the piece of transplanted stomach now has no nerve supply, it must have been stimulated by a hormone.

We now have some idea of what causes the stomach to secrete. We want to ask how stomach movements and secretions are coordinated with processes taking place in other parts of the GI tract. When we place fat in the small intestine of an animal with a transplanted piece of stomach, the transplanted tissue stops producing gastric juice. Since the transplanted piece of stomach is not attached to any intact nervous structure, it is reasonable to suspect that its secretion is controlled by a hormone. Further experiments indicate that the presence of fat in the small intestine stimulates the secretion of a hormone called **enterogastrone** into the blood. Upon reaching the stomach, enterogastrone inhibits the secretion of gastric juices and also inhibits movements of materials in the stomach. Slowing the stomach activity whenever food (for example, fat) arrives in the intestine is an advantage; digestion in the intestine will now have time to take place without being displaced by any further emptying of the stomach.

The Liver and Pancreas

The liver and the pancreas both deliver secretions to the digestive system. The secretions of the pancreas are particularly important. They include enzymes of the three basic types: **proteases, amylases,** and **lipases.** In addition to the enzyme portion of its secretions, the pancreas also adds a large quantity of the basic bicarbonate ion which is important in the neutralization of the hydrochloric acid secreted by the stomach. The secretions of the pancreas are controlled by hormones and nerve reflexes. They are carried to the gastro-intestinal tract by a duct (Fig. 10.2) which leads to the upper part of the small intestine (**duodenum**). In addition to these digestive secretions, the pancreas also produces endocrine hormones which it delivers without a duct into the blood stream (see the next chapter).

The common bile duct of the liver enters the duodenum, along with the pancreatic duct. Through this duct the liver secretes a material called **bile.** Bile helps break up large collections of fat molecules into smaller ones. This is called **emulsification**

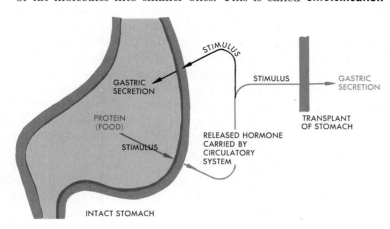

Fig. 9.5 When food is placed in the stomach, the stomach transplant secretes gastric juices, even though the nerve supply to the transplant no longer exists. This demonstrates *hormonal control* of gastric secretion.

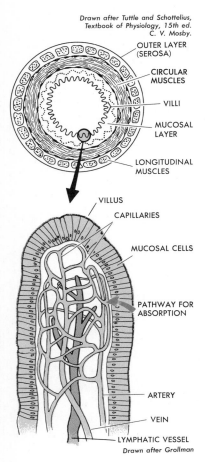

Drawn after Tuttle and Schottelius,
Textbook of Physiology, 15th ed.
C. V. Mosby.

OUTER LAYER
(SEROSA)

CIRCULAR
MUSCLES

VILLI

MUCOSAL
LAYER

LONGITUDINAL
MUSCLES

VILLUS

CAPILLARIES

MUCOSAL CELLS

PATHWAY FOR
ABSORPTION

ARTERY

VEIN

LYMPHATIC VESSEL
Drawn after Grollman

Fig. 9.6 *Mucosal* cells form the inner lining of the small intestine (cross-section at top). These cells are specialized to absorb digested foods and provide the pathway for food to enter the blood circulation.

It is the same general process that allows oil and water to mix when you wash your hands with soap (since the soap is an emulsifier). When occurring in the intestine, emulsification allows more lipase molecules to come into close association with the lipid, thus increasing the breakdown of lipid into fatty acids and glycerol.

The Small Intestine

A series of enzymes secreted by the cells of the small intestine complete the digestion of food. From Table 9-2, you will see that these include 1. erepsin which acts on small clusters of amino acids (called **peptides**), splitting them into the individual amino acids; and 2. other enzymes that split double sugars into simple sugars.

ABSORPTION AND MOTILITY

The secretion of digestive juices which split food into elementary building blocks is only one of the processes taking place in the GI tract. Next, the building blocks must be absorbed into the blood, and material within the tract must be moved along the length of the tube. A closer look at the structure of the tubular walls of the GI tract will help us understand these processes.

In Fig. 9.6 (top), we see a section made by cutting across the intestine (cross-section). The intestine is composed of three basic layers: 1. the innermost layer, or **mucosal layer**, which is richly supplied with blood vessels and contains cells responsible for the secretion of enzymes, the production of mucous, and the absorption of digested food. 2. The middle layer is a **muscular layer.** Some smooth muscles wrap around the cylindrical tube in a circular manner, while other smooth muscle cells run longitudinally up and down the length of the intestine. These muscles, which are influenced by autonomic nerve fibers, are responsible for the movement of material through the gastro-intestinal tract. 3. The outer layer of the intestines is composed of **fibrous connective tissue** which is covered for the most part by thin, flattened cells lining the inside of the abdominal cavity and covering many of the internal organs.

Absorption: In the bottom part of Fig. 9.6 we see that in order to reach the blood stream, materials must travel across the mucosal cells. This important process occurs almost exclusively in the intestines, but the mechanisms of absorption are poorly

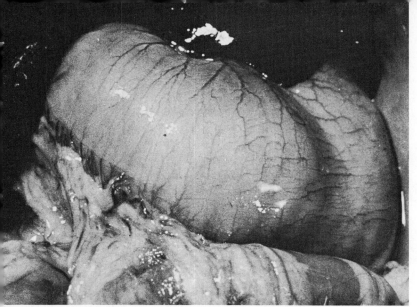

Encyclopedia Britannica Films

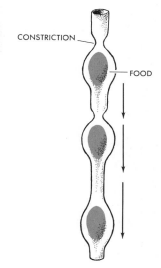

Fig. 9.7 *Peristalsis* (in the esophagus, stomach, and intestines) moves food along the GI tract by waves of constriction that squeeze the food forward. The photograph shows one such wave in the stomach.

CONSTRICTION

FOOD

understood. Some substances simply diffuse into the blood stream whenever their concentrations in the intestine is higher than in the blood. Other substances, such as simple sugars and amino acids, are actively transported so that they are absorbed even in low concentrations. In addition to nutritional components, the large amounts of fluid that are secreted into the tract must be reabsorbed into the body.

Whatever the mechanism, the speed of absorption is increased many times because of the peculiar structure of the mucosal surface. You can see that the intestinal surface is not smooth because of the many finger-like projections called **villi.** The villi increase the amount of mucosal surface available to the digested material. After the nutrients have been absorbed into the blood they are further processed by other cells of the body.

Motility: Material not absorbed by the GI tract must be removed to make room for fresh food. On the other hand, movement of material through the tract must not be so fast that the complex foods we eat are removed before they can be digested and absorbed. In other words, food must be moved through the system slowly enough so that each process has time enough to take place. On the average, food remains in the stomach from about two to four hours. After it is passed to the intestines, it takes many more hours before the undigested material is eliminated.

Food is moved along the GI tract by a process called **peristalsis.** This occurs in the esophagus, stomach, and intestines. It is caused by constriction resulting from contraction of the circularly arranged smooth muscles. As Fig. 9.7 shows, this constriction is a local one. It progresses down the length of the gastro-intestinal tract and, in a sense, squeezes the food along the length of the tract much in the same way as toothpaste is squeezed from a tube. The net effect of peristalsis is that the contents are pushed down the length of the GI tract toward the anus.

Other types of movements besides peristalsis also occur. One of the most important of these motions is the churning and the mixing that occurs in the stomach. The speed and the strength of gastric and intestinal contractions is controlled by the autonomic nervous system, by a slow spread of nerve impulses originating in a network of nerve fibers located entirely within the GI tract, and by the hormonal environment. These controlling mechanisms coordinate movements of the different parts of the tract. For example, the digestion of a large meal may be followed by an urge to defecate. This is partly due to a reflex initiated by mechanical distention of the stomach and duodenum, resulting in massive peristaltic movements in the lower parts of the large intestine. In general, excitation of parasympathetic nerves speeds the propulsion of material through the tract, while excitation of sympathetic nerves does the opposite.

Absorbed nutrients are transported by the blood to various organs of the body. Some of these nutrients are used by the cells for their energy content; others are used for growth and repair of cell structures; still others are stored for future use. These many processes do not occur in a haphazard way. They are balanced and delicately controlled. We shall see some examples of this in the next chapter.

SUMMARY

To enter the internal environment, food must be transported across the cellular walls of the GI tract into the blood stream— it must be **absorbed.** There is only a small variety of molecules absorbed by the GI tract. **Carbohydrates** must be broken into **simple sugars; proteins** into **amino acids;** and **fats** into **glycerol** and **fatty acids.** This digestion of food is accelerated by specific **enzymes** secreted by the walls of the GI tract and certain glands associated with the tract.

Digestive enzymes are not secreted continuously. They are controlled by nerve reflexes, hormones, and mechanical stimulation of the walls of the GI tract. Absorption occurs in the intestines. While some substances are absorbed by diffusion, others, such as simple sugars and amino acids, are actively transported into the blood stream, so they are absorbed even if they are present at low concentrations.

Food is moved along the GI tract by **peristalsis,** which occurs in the esophagus, stomach, and intestines. It is caused by a progressive constriction, which results from the contraction of the circularly arranged smooth muscles. This constriction progresses down the length of the tract and squeezes the food along. The movements of the GI tract are controlled by nerve impulses and by hormones. **Parasympathetic** nerve impulses speed movements through the tract, while **sympathetic** nerve impulses do the opposite.

FOR THOUGHT AND DISCUSSION

1 Suppose that you eat a hamburger. The bun is rich in carbohydrate; the meat is rich in protein, fat, and some indigestable matter. Trace the fate of the hamburger from the time it enters your mouth until it leaves the GI tract. What enzymes are involved, where are they secreted, how are they controlled?

2 A peptic ulcer is an open sore in the wall of the stomach or duodenum. It occurs more frequently in persons subjected to continual stress and anxiety. Peptic ulcers are believed to be caused by the digestive action of excessive gastric juice secretions. It is sometimes treated by cutting the vagus nerve supply to the stomach (vagotomy). Discuss the basis and physiological implications of this treatment.

SELECTED READINGS

Bayliss, W. P. and E. H. Starling. "The Mechanism of Pancreatic Secretion," in *Great Experiments in Biology*. Englewood Cliffs, New Jersey: Prentice-Hall, Inc., 1955, p. 60.

Carlson, A. J., V. Johnson, and H. M. Cavert. *The Machinery of the Body*, 5th Ed. Chicago: University of Chicago Press, 1961.

Davenport, H. W. *The Physiology of the Digestive Tract*, 2nd Ed. Chicago: Year Book Medical Publishers Inc., 1961.

Guyton, A. C. *Textbook of Medical Physiology*, 3rd Ed. Philadelphia: W. B. Saunders Co., 1966.

10 METABOLISM AND HORMONES

Fig. 10.1 The islet cells of the pancreas (color) secrete a small protein called *insulin*. Without this vital protein the body starves in the midst of plenty, for it cannot convert glucose into useful energy. People who cannot produce their own insulin have the disease *diabetes mellitus*.

Eric V. Gravé

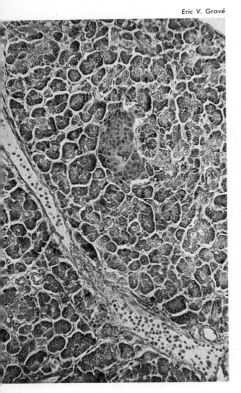

In 1889, the two German physiologists Joseph von Mering and Oscar Minkowski began a study that led to the solution of an age-old mystery. They wanted to know what, if any, disturbances in digestion would result if they removed the pancreas glands from dogs. After they operated on several dogs the animals began to show many deficiencies, and after a short time they died. Why? The operation had been a simple one. The pancreas glands secrete digestive juices, but they are not the only source of digestive juices. Apparently the glands had some special function. Although the dogs had hearty appetites after the operation, they lost weight and lacked energy and muscular strength. Further, they began to use stored fat and cellular protein for the energy required just to keep alive. These and other symptoms were very similar to those of starvation.

von Mering and Minkowski soon found that the problems facing these animals were far more profound than simple starvation. One curious thing they noticed was that ants gathered in the kennels where the sick dogs were kept, and the ants were attracted in greatest numbers to those places where the dogs had urinated. Why? There were no gatherings of ants in the kennels of the healthy dogs. von Mering and Minkowski found that the blood sugar (glucose) level in the sick animals was abnormally high—so high that the animals were excreting large amounts of it into their urine. Although there was plenty of blood sugar available, these animals were not able to use it; they were "starving" in the midst of plenty. This is precisely what happens to people who have the disease called **diabetes mellitus** if they are not treated. The experiments of von Mering and Minkowski were to prove that the pancreas was associated with this disease.

Further research has shown that most of the "starvation" symptoms which occur either in diabetes or following removal of the pancreas are not due to disturbances in digestion; instead they result from an inability to use glucose. This can be demonstrated simply by tying-off the pancreatic ducts leading from the

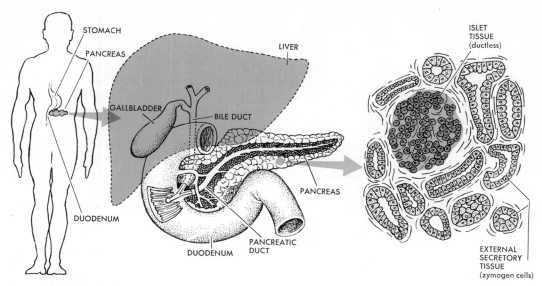

Fig. 10.2 The pancreas is a dual organ. Zymogen cells secrete digestive enzymes into the pancreatic duct, which conveys the enzymes to the duodenum. Islet cells secrete insulin into the circulating blood.

pancreas to the duodenum. This prevents the pancreatic secretions from reaching the GI tract. Although the animal will have digestive disturbances, he can still use glucose, he does not develop diabetic symptoms, and he will not die. However, if the pancreas is removed, the animal loses the ability to use glucose, diabetic symptoms appear, and the animal dies.

Apparently, in addition to secreting digestive enzymes, the pancreas is involved with the animal's capacity to use glucose. This dual role of the pancreas is better understood if we examine its microscopic structure. Figure 10.2 shows that the pancreas is made up of two types of cells. One type, called **zymogen** cells, makes up a tubular network ending in dilated sacs called **alveoli.** The ducts of the many alveoli contained within the pancreas unite and give rise to the ducts of the pancreas which carry the pancreatic digestive enzymes to the small intestine. The other type of cells is found among the alveoli in small clumps, or "islands." They are called **islet** cells. When the ducts are tied off, the zymogen cells degenerate, but the islet cells remain healthy. The fact that animals in which the ducts have been tied off do not develop diabetes suggests that the islet cells are required for the normal use of glucose by other cells of the body.

How do the islet cells exert an influence on other cells? One possibility is that they secrete into the circulating blood a hormone which is needed for glucose utilization. If this is true, then we might expect to find high concentrations of the hormone within the islet cells, where it is produced. This can be demonstrated by first tying off the pancreatic ducts in an animal so that the zymogen cells degenerate, but leaving healthy islet cells. We then remove the pancreas, mince it, and soak it in a salt

111

solution. The resulting solution, containing many materials which have escaped from the islet cells, is called an **extract.** If we inject some of the extract into a diabetic animal, all symptoms of diabetes disappear! One of the substances in the extract is the hormone we are looking for; it is a small protein called **insulin.**

We have just described a common pattern for the study of **endocrine** (hormone producing) glands: 1. the gland is removed and the resulting symptoms are recorded. 2. Various extracts of the gland are injected back into the animal until we find an active one that relieves the symptoms. 3. We then examine the various components of the extract in hopes of finding which chemical is responsible for the activity of the extract—that is, which chemical is the hormone. But this is not the end of our search. We also want to know how the hormone influences cellular activities, how a lack of hormones leads to the gross symptoms that we observe, and how the secretion of hormones is controlled.

Function of Insulin

Many experiments suggest that one function of insulin is to make cells more permeable to glucose. This would explain why the diabetic cannot use glucose. If the sugar cannot get into these cells, the cells cannot use it and have to turn to other sources for energy—fat and protein. Despite the fact that little or no sugar can enter many of the body cells in the diabetic, glucose continues to be absorbed into the blood from the GI tract. As a result, the concentration of blood sugar rises to such high values that it cannot be reabsorbed by the kidney tubules, and large amounts of glucose escape into the urine. The excessive urine sugar is accompanied by an equivalent excess of water. (Recall from Chapter 8 how osmotic forces determine water excretion by the kidney.) This extra excretion of water explains the large flow of urine invariably found in the diabetic. In fact, the loss of body fluid (through excessive urine formation) can become so great in the untreated diabetic that it can lead to a collapse of the circulation, and death.

Control of Insulin Secretion

In the normal animal, insulin secretion is controlled by the circulating blood glucose as shown by the feedback loop in Fig. 10.3. Blood glucose stimulates insulin secretion by the pancreas so that when blood glucose levels are high, more insulin is secreted. The extra insulin increases glucose utilization (probably because it increases cell membrane permeability to glucose) and the blood glucose level falls back toward normal.

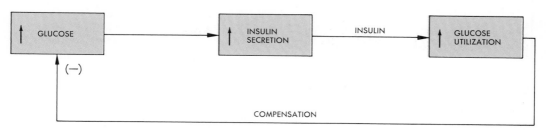

Fig. 10.3 A high concentration of glucose in the blood stimulates the secretion of insulin. The feedback loop shows how this response helps to stabilize the blood glucose concentration.

However, if the blood glucose level falls, less insulin is secreted, resulting in a smaller amount of glucose used and a consequent rise in the blood glucose level back toward normal. Here we see a simple feedback system which, in this instance, helps stabilize the level of blood glucose. However, blood glucose as well as tissue fat and protein are strongly influenced by a number of hormones and other factors, in addition to insulin. In order to understand them, we must first examine some of the inter-relations between carbohydrates, fats, and proteins.

METABOLISM

Figures 10.4 A, B, C are simplified diagrams of some of the chemical transformations that take place within body cells. These reactions plus all the other chemical reactions taking place in the body are collectively called **metabolism.**

There are several reactions within the cell that liberate useful energy. Figure 10.4A shows that each of the three primary building blocks—fatty acids (and glycerol), glucose, and amino acids —can be broken down within the cell. If oxygen is present, carbon dioxide and water are formed. During the process, energy is liberated, part of it is lost as heat but part is trapped and stored through the formation of ATP. These steps are indicated by processes 1, 2, and 3 in the figure. The ATP can be used by the "machinery" of the cell (step 4) for a variety of purposes: for example, to supply energy for muscle contraction, secretion, and synthesis of complicated molecules.

In contrast to energy-yielding reactions that break molecules into smaller pieces, cells are capable of many synthetic reactions that require energy. In these reactions the primary building blocks are combined into larger molecules. Step 7 in Fig. 10.4B shows that many molecules of glucose can be combined and stored in the form of **glycogen** (animal starch). This occurs primarily in liver and in muscle. In times of need, the liver glycogen breaks down (step 8) and liberates glucose to the blood.

113

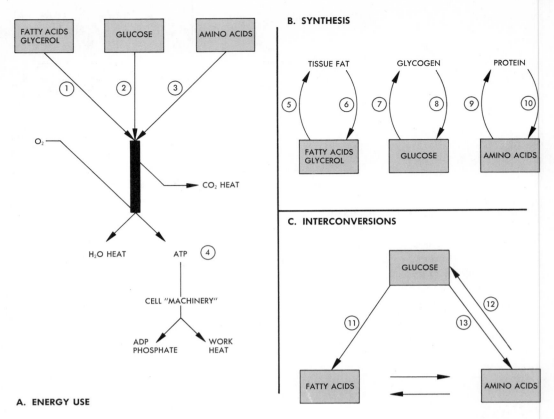

Fig. 10.4 In addition to breaking down molecules, cells can build up, or *synthesize*, large molecules. This diagram shows that the three principal foodstuffs—carbohydrates, fats, and proteins—are broken down, built up, and reconverted, depending on the cell's energy needs.

Similarly, fatty acids are combined with glycerol to form fat, which is stored in fat tissues distributed throughout the body (step 5). Finally (step 9), the amino acids can be strung together into huge protein molecules which form structural parts of cells, enzymes, plasma proteins, and other body constituents.

Figure 10.4C also shows that the three principal foodstuffs—carbohydrates, fats, and amino acids—can be interconverted. Through a sequence of steps (11 and 5), glucose can be used to form tissue fat. This often occurs when you eat too much carbohydrate. The amount of carbohydrate that can be stored as glycogen is not very large, but this is not true of tissue fat. Accordingly, excessive amounts of glucose are converted into tissue fat. Finally, steps 13 and 12 show that glucose can also be converted to amino acids, and amino acids into glucose.

From Fig. 10.4 we can again see some of the problems faced by the diabetic, who is not able to make use of glucose. Step 2 is blocked, yet the work of the body must continue. Since glucose cannot be tapped as a source of energy, fatty acids (step 1) and amino acids (step 3) must be broken down, and eventually so must tissue fat and tissue protein.

114

Hormones and Energy Release

The metabolic scheme that we have outlined in Fig. 10.4 is influenced by several hormones. We can get some idea of the complexities involved by examining how they control the blood sugar, or glucose, level. In a normal person the blood sugar remains relatively constant despite the fact that his dietary intake of carbohydrate is very irregular. The liver (Fig. 10.5) which serves as a storage depot for carbohydrates plays an important role in this regulation. Immediately after a meal, while food is being absorbed, blood sugar is carried by the blood from the gastrointestinal tract to the liver, where a large part of it is stored as glycogen (step 7 in Fig. 10.4). At this time the blood entering the liver contains more glucose than does the blood leaving the liver. Later, when absorption is complete, the reverse is true. Blood leaving the liver is richer in glucose than is blood entering it. We conclude that the liver is now breaking down some of its stored glycogen (step 8 in Fig. 10.4), releasing it as glucose, thus helping to replenish blood glucose as it is used by other tissues.

The release of glucose from the liver is accelerated by the action of adrenalin (**epinepherine**), a hormone secreted by the adrenal medulla. You will recall from previous chapters that adrenalin is secreted in times of stress. During such times it aids the animal by providing him with glucose from the liver (step 8 in Fig. 10.4).

The liver contains enough glycogen to supply body tissues with glucose for several hours. However, when the supply of glycogen becomes low, protein and fat are broken down. This use of protein and fat is thought to be controlled by secretions from the adrenal cortex (Fig. 10.6) and the anterior pituitary (Fig. 10.7). **Cortisol,** one of many hormones secreted by the adrenal cortex, promotes the use of protein. For example, during fasting, cortisol induces the passage of amino acids from tissue protein into the liver where they are converted to glucose (steps 10 and 12 in Fig. 10.4). Cortisol is also necessary for the effective breakdown of fat. If your adrenal glands were removed, you would develop a low blood sugar within 12 to 24 hours after you stopped eating. However, the presence of adrenal glands helps you to maintain a normal level of blood glucose, even during many days of fasting.

One of the hormones secreted by the anterior pituitary gland, called **growth hormone,** plays an equally important role in the regulation of blood glucose. This hormone promotes the mobilization of fat from tissue deposits, making the fat available as an energy source (steps 6 and 1 in Fig. 10.4). It also inhibits the use of glucose. The action of growth hormone seems to switch the source of cellular fuel from carbohydrate to fat. Thus, its action

Fig. 10.5 The liver plays an important role in regulating the blood sugar (glucose) level. In a normal person, glucose is stored or released as it is needed.

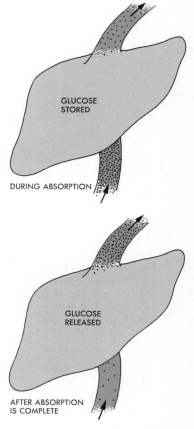

GLUCOSE STORED

DURING ABSORPTION

GLUCOSE RELEASED

AFTER ABSORPTION IS COMPLETE

DOTS REPRESENT GLUCOSE

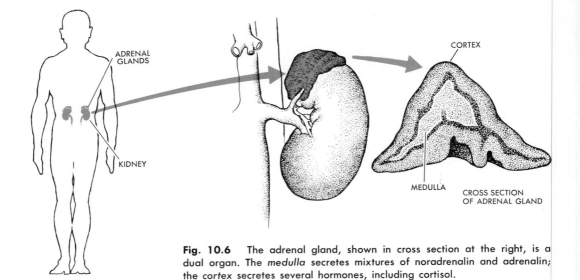

Fig. 10.6 The adrenal gland, shown in cross section at the right, is a dual organ. The *medulla* secretes mixtures of noradrenalin and adrenalin; the *cortex* secretes several hormones, including cortisol.

seems to be antagonistic to insulin. We can demonstrate this in a dramatic way: if we remove the pancreas from an animal, the animal develops diabetes. However, if we next remove the anterior pituitary gland, so that the source of growth hormone is cut off, the diabetic symptoms are greatly diminished! This experiment does not mean that removal of the pituitary gland is a cure for diabetes, but simply that under such conditions the diabetic symptoms disappear. An animal that has had both glands removed becomes very unhealthy.

Despite the antagonistic actions of insulin and growth hormone, the secretion of both hormones is *controlled* so that they work together and help stabilize the blood glucose. Recent experiments suggest that a low blood glucose stimulates the secretion of growth hormone. This promotes cellular use of fat rather than glucose and the metabolic machinery is no longer as dependent on the low level of glucose. One result is that the blood glucose level may increase back toward normal. If these ideas are correct, the interaction between blood glucose and growth hormone provides us with the homeostatic feedback

Fig. 10.7 Secretions of the anterior pituitary gland stimulate the activity of several other glands; it also secretes growth hormone.

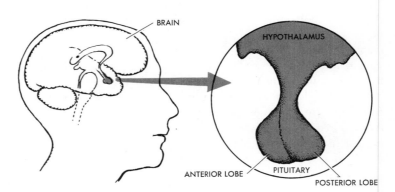

116

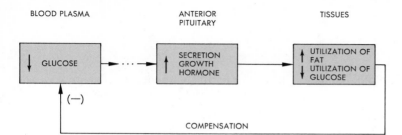

Fig. 10.8   Growth hormone is secreted in response to a low concentration
of blood glucose. The feedback loop shows how this response may help
stabilize the blood glucose concentration.

loop illustrated in Fig. 10.8. Compare this with the control of
insulin illustrated in Fig. 10.3.

One other hormone affecting the processes outlined in Fig.
10.4 is **thyroxin.** This hormone is secreted by the thyroid gland
(Fig. 10.9) and seems to play a role in the regulation of the over-
all metabolic rate. With excessive thyroid activity, oxygen consumption of most cells is increased above normal. With subnormal levels of thyroid hormone oxygen consumption is reduced.

Hormones and Growth

We have already mentioned two hormones
which are very important in normal growth, one of them being
growth hormone. Growth hormone plays a very important role
by promoting the entry of amino acids into cells and by further
promoting the incorporation of these amino acids into proteins
(step 9 in Fig. 10.4). In short, it strongly influences the growth
of cellular structures. Its effects are dramatically revealed if
growth hormone secretion during childhood is abnormal. With
subnormal amounts of growth hormone a child will never reach
adult size; he will be a dwarf. However, excessive secretion during

Fig. 10.9   Thyroxin helps regulate the over-all metabolic rate. It is
secreted by cells of the thyroid gland and stored in the follicles (see cover
photograph).

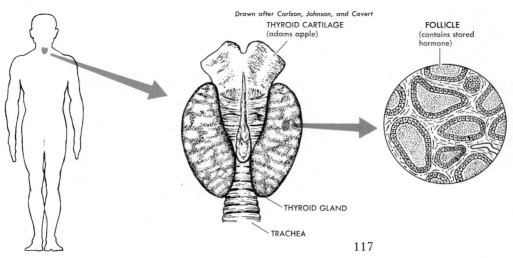

Drawn after Carlson, Johnson, and Cavert
THYROID CARTILAGE
(adams apple)

FOLLICLE
(contains stored
hormone)

THYROID GLAND

TRACHEA

117

childhood and adolescence results in abnormally fast growth and produces a giant. Figure 10.10 shows a dwarf compared with a giant. Both suffered from abnormal growth hormone secretions during childhood.

Thyroxin also plays a role in incorporating amino acids into protein and so influences growth in the child and adolescent. In children with very poor thyroid function, growth will be stunted. There will also be a retardation in mental, physical, and sexual development. If the condition remains untreated, the person will be a sterile dwarf with an intelligence that may never exceed that of a five-year-old.

Hormone Control: the "Master Gland" and Hypothalamus

The anterior pituitary is often referred to as the "master gland" because it secretes several hormones required by other glands. These include the thyroid, the adrenal cortex, and the sex glands (discussed in Chapter 12). However, recent experiments have shown that the anterior pituitary, in turn, seems to be controlled by secretions originating in the central nervous system, specifically from the **hypothalamus,** which is located at the base of the brain, very close to the pituitary (see Fig. 10.7).

Let us consider interactions between the pituitary gland and thyroid as an illustration of this type of control. The anterior pituitary secretes a hormone called **thyroid-stimulating-hormone,** abbreviated **TSH.** As its name implies, TSH stimulates the thyroid glands, promoting the glands' growth and secretory activity. The resulting secretion of thyroxin in turn acts on the pituitary gland, depressing further TSH secretion. Thus, we have a control loop which stabilizes the level of circulating thyroxin.

If, for some reason, the thyroxin level gets too high, it will depress the secretion of TSH, which in turn will depress the production and secretion of thyroxin so that its concentration in the blood will return to normal. However, if the thyroxin level is reduced, then its inhibiting effect on the secretion of TSH will also be reduced; the production of TSH will then be increased, resulting in a greater secretion of thyroxin. This feedback regulation is shown in Fig. 10.11.

The description we have given explains how a constant level of thyroxin can be maintained in the circulating blood. However, it does not explain how the secretion of the hormone changes and meets changing demands of the body. A good guess would be that the changing needs of the body are "sensed" by the hypothalamus, which, in turn, influences the release of TSH. For example, in a cold environment the hypothalamus secretes a substance which stimulates the secretion of TSH. This, in turn,

Fig. 10.10 During childhood, an abnormally high secretion of growth hormone causes excessive growth (giantism). An abnormally low secretion inhibits growth (dwarfism).

Ewing Galloway

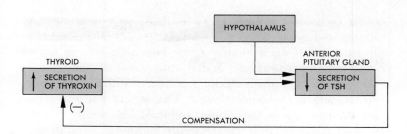

stimulates the secretion of thyroxin, and, finally, thyroxin stimulates general body metabolism. The net result is greater heat production within the body, thus enabling the animal to withstand the cold environment and maintain homeostasis.

A similar process controls the secretion of cortisol by the adrenal cortex. The anterior pituitary secretes another hormone called **ACTH,** which promotes the growth and secretion of the adrenal cortex. The secretion of ACTH, in turn, is inhibited by cortisol, and stimulated by secretions from the hypothalamus.

Hormonal Mechanisms

In recent years physiologists have done a great deal of research to find out how hormones exert such a strong influence on metabolism. Some hormones, such as insulin, are known to change the permeability of cell membranes and, therefore, regulate the amount of materials made available to the metabolic machinery. However, this explanation does not apply to all hormones, nor even to all of the actions of insulin. This means that we must look for other possibilities.

A promising suggestion is that hormones act by promoting the activities of cellular enzymes. Most of the chemical reactions occurring within a cell take place on the surface of large protein enzyme molecules. Without these enzymes the reactions would be too slow to be of any importance. The presence of hormones may be necessary for certain of these enzymes to work, or the hormones may influence the actual synthesis of specific protein enzymes. Evidence supporting this latter possibility has come out of experiments in which physiologists have used specific antibiotics known to interfere with protein synthesis. These same antibiotics have inhibited the actions of a number of hormones.

HEAT AND BODY TEMPERATURE

Roughly one-half of the energy liberated by decomposition of carbohydrate, protein, or fat is captured in the form of ATP. The rest of the energy is lost as heat. The ATP formed eventually is used up as the body does work—lifting, running, and so on. Since no process is 100 per cent efficient in converting all of the available energy into work, we can expect to find some heat produced during most physical activity.

Despite the continuous heat production within your body, your temperature remains constant. This means that heat is lost from the body just as fast as it is produced. This ability to regulate body temperature is advantageous, because changes in temperature cause changes in the rates of chemical reactions. Cooling or heating could upset a number of chemical reaction sequences which must be delicately balanced if the body is to function well. Animals like frogs, which cannot regulate their body temperature, are at the mercy of their environment. When the weather cools, their body temperature falls, their metabolism slows, and they become very sluggish.

What, actually, is body temperature? If you hold a thermometer against your skin you get a reading quite different from the reading when you hold the thermometer under your tongue. The temperature that we measure under the tongue corresponds fairly well with the temperature that we would measure in any of the vital organs—heart, liver, or the intestines. It is this inner, or **core temperature** (temperature of the vital organs) that we mean by "body temperature." The core temperature is well regulated by the body, rarely falling below 97 or rising above 104 Fahrenheit degrees.

The temperature measured on the skin is called the **surface temperature.** It fluctuates much more than the core temperature, rising and falling with the temperature of the environment. The correspondence between the core temperature and the surface temperature depends on the blood flow to the skin. If the blood flow to the skin is large, then the surface temperature will begin to approach the core temperature. When the blood flow to the skin diminishes, the surface temperature tends to approximate the environmental temperature.

If the temperature of the body is to remain constant the heat produced must just balance the heat lost. The processes whereby heat can be produced and heat can be lost are illustrated in Fig. 10.12.

Heat Production

Your body produces heat even when you are resting. The heat that is produced by the metabolism required just to keep you alive and awake is called the **basal metabolic heat.** Over and above the basal metabolic heat, muscular activity such as exercising or shivering also produces heat. In addition

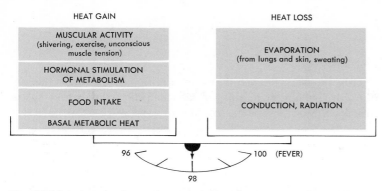

Fig. 10.12 Because heat gain is balanced by heat loss, our body temperature tends to remain constant.

to muscular activity, hormones can influence the production of heat through their influence on metabolism. This is particularly true of thyroxin and adrenalin. It is by variations in muscular activity and the quantity of circulating hormones that heat production in your body frequently changes.

Heat Loss

You may lose heat by radiation and conduction from the surface of your body. The amount of heat you lose this way depends on the difference in temperature between the surface of your body and the environment. The greater the difference, the greater the heat loss will be. In order for heat to be lost, of course, the surface of your body must be at a higher temperature than that of the environment. If the environmental temperature rises above your body temperature, you will not lose heat by radiation or conduction; instead, your body will gain heat from the environment.

A second very important method of losing heat is through evaporation. When you come out of the water after swimming, water evaporates from your skin and you feel cool. In order for water to evaporate, the water molecules must have a certain minimum amount of energy. The faster moving molecules can overcome the forces holding them in the liquid state and bound off into the air as gas (water vapor) molecules. The slower and, therefore, cooler molecules are left behind. Heat then flows from the warmer surface of your skin to the cooler water molecules. This flow of heat transfers energy to the water, speeding the water molecules up so that more of them escape. This cooling of your skin surface also cools any blood which tends to flow through that part of your body. Sweating is an obvious way to lose heat by evaporation. However, in addition to sweating, some water is continually lost by processes that we are normally not aware of. Water continuously evaporates from the skin. There is also a small loss of water from the surface of the lungs when you breathe. The amount of water that evaporates—when you

121

breathe or sweat—depends on the humidity of the air. When the humidity is high, water evaporates much more slowly and, therefore contributes less to the cooling process.

Temperature Regulation

Control of body temperature depends on the **hypothalamus.** It acts as a thermostat and responds to the temperature of the blood bathing it, and to nerve impulses that come from temperature receptors in the skin. It is the front part, or anterior hypothalamus, that responds to heat. We can either stimulate this part electrically or heat it up and get several responses which increase heat loss. These include 1. sweat secretion, which increases heat loss by evaporation; and 2. dilation of blood vessels in the skin, which causes the surface temperature of the body to approximate the core temperature, with the result that more heat is lost by conduction and radiation. Signals for these responses travel over sympathetic nerves. If we destroy the anterior hypothalamus there will be no response to heat.

The rear portion, or posterior hypothalamus, responds to cold. If we chill the blood surrounding this part of the hypothalamus, any sweating that may be occurring at the time stops. Also, the blood vessels in the skin constrict, minimizing the heat exchange between the core and the cool surface of the body. In addition to preventing excessive heat loss, the hypothalamus is involved in regulating heat production. Chilling, for example, causes shivering and a hormonal discharge which increases body metabolism. These two responses increase heat production. The feedback loop which is involved in controlling temperature is illustrated in Fig. 10.13.

Fever and the Body's Thermostat

The hypothalamus acts as a thermostat which is set to maintain a temperature of 98.6°F. Sometimes this thermostat setting will be altered. Although the precise mechanism is obscure, we know that this occurs during infection and when products of tissue destruction are introduced into the blood stream. In both cases a fever results. Although the body's temperature regulation machinery is operating, the thermostat seems to be set at an abnormal level.

At the onset of fever, even though your body temperature is normal, the body responds as if it were too cold. You begin to shiver and the blood vessels in the skin constrict causing pale, dry skin, and decreased heat loss. Finally your metabolism may step up, with a resulting increase in heat production. All of

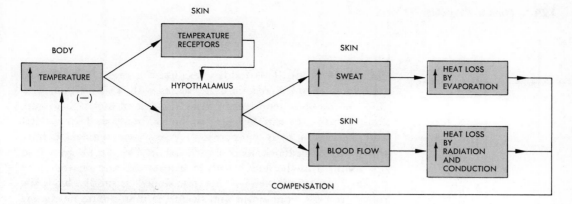

these factors tend to raise your temperature. This continues until the temperature settles at the new high-level setting. When fever is on the decline the opposite response occurs. Your skin becomes flushed, indicating that the blood vessels of the skin have expanded and you begin to sweat. Both of these responses lower your body temperature by increasing its heat loss.

Response to Intense Heat

Suppose that you go into a room that has an air temperature of about 110°F. Radiation and conduction do not work in your favor. Instead of losing heat from the surface of your body to the surroundings, you gain heat. You can survive, but now sweating is the only mechanism you have for losing heat.

The normal response to intense heat strains the circulatory system. This follows because the hypothalamus responds to the increased heat by causing the blood vessels in your skin to expand. This leads to a decreased resistance to blood flow and your blood pressure tends to fall. Reflexes which prevent large changes in blood pressure (see Chapter 5) then begin to operate, and the decreased resistance to blood flow is compensated for by the heart working harder. The expanded blood vessels make it possible for large amounts of blood to pool in the vessels of your skin at the expense of other organs. If, as a result, the blood supply to your brain becomes sufficiently low, you will faint.

Sweating may also create a circulatory problem because of the salt and water loss. Excessive fluid loss causes a decreased plasma volume. This may slow down the output of blood from the heart, which could lead to decreased blood flow to the skin which, in turn, could reduce sweating. If this happened, your main avenue for heat loss would be closed. In that event heat production would continue and your body temperature would rise until your whole system collapsed.

The body's ability to control heat loss is limited. *When heat cannot be lost rapidly enough to prevent a rise in body temperature,* a vicious

Fig. 10.13 An increase in temperature of the body surface or blood acts on the hypothalamus, which controls the sweat glands and blood vessels in the skin. The feedback loop shows how the hypothalamus responds and stabilizes body temperature. Can you draw the corresponding feedback loop to show the response to cold?

123

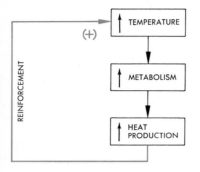

Fig. 10.14 The body's ability to control heat loss is limited. If heat gain increases beyond the body's ability to compensate, positive feedback throws the system out of control, as shown by this feedback loop.

circle may occur. This follows because the rate of metabolism (like most chemical reactions) increases with a rise in temperature. As the body temperature rises, the rate of metabolism and, consequently, the rate of heat production increase. This accelerates the rise in body temperature. When heat regulation fails, the positive feedback loop illustrated in Fig. 10.14 goes into operation; if unchecked it ends in heat stroke and death.

The best defense against this intense heat is simple: leave the room! You use your brain and decide to manipulate or change the external environment until it no longer poses a threat. Interactions between brain and environment are taken up in the next chapter.

SUMMARY

Many of the chemical transformations taking place within the body are controlled by hormones. Hormone secretions, in turn, are subjected to complex feedback regulation.

Insulin promotes the use of glucose by making some cells more permeable to glucose. A high blood glucose stimulates secretion of insulin and, as a result of its action, insulin helps maintain a stable concentration of glucose in the blood.

Growth hormone promotes the use of fat, inhibits the use of glucose, and helps regulate the level of blood glucose. Further, it promotes the incorporation of amino acids into proteins and is essential for growth.

Thyroxin stimulates oxygen consumption and plays an important role in regulating the metabolic rate. It is also important in growth. Children with deficient thyroid secretions will be retarded in their mental and physical development. The growth and secretion of the thyroid gland is controlled by TSH (secreted by the anterior pituitary). The secretion of TSH is, in turn, controlled by thyroxin and secretions from the hypothalamus.

Cortisol promotes the formation of glucose from amino acids in the liver. Secretion of cortisol is controlled by ACTH (secreted by the anterior pituitary). The secretion of ACTH is, in turn, controlled by cortisol and secretions from the hypothalamus.

The work and metabolism of the body is always accompanied by the liberation of heat. Nevertheless, the body temperature (core temperature) remains constant; heat production balances heat loss. The hypothalamus is a center for temperature regulation. It responds to the temperature of the blood that comes to it and to nerve impulses that come from temperature receptors in the skin. Heating the hypothalamus results in sweat secretion and dilation of blood vessels in the skin. Chilling the hypothalamus results in decreased heat loss (inhibition of sweat secretion and constriction of blood vessels in the skin) and increased heat production (shivering and an increase in body metabolism).

FOR THOUGHT AND DISCUSSION

1 If the liver is removed from an animal, how will its blood glucose be affected? Explain.

2 Around 1900, researchers tried to make hormonal extracts of the entire pancreas gland, which contained both islet cells and zymogen cells, but they all failed. Can you suggest a reason for their failure? (HINT: in addition to secreting insulin what are the other functions of the pancreas?)

3 Experimental research procedures used in the study of hormones include: (a) removal of glands (elimination of hormones); (b) replacement of hormones; and (c) overdoses of hormones. Keeping these procedures in mind, design experiments to demonstrate the dependence of the thyroid on the pituitary gland.

4 A man is lost in the hot desert without water. What physiological responses have you studied in this and in preceding chapters that will tend to help him survive?

5 After exposure to cold, your lips may turn blue. The color is due to the high content of reduced hemoglobin in the blood supplying the skin. Why does cold bring about this response?

SELECTED READINGS

Baldwin, E. B. *The Nature of Biochemistry*. New York: Cambridge University Press, 1962.

Benziger, T. H. "The Human Thermostat," *Scientific American* (January 1961).

Davidson, E. H. "Hormones and Genes," *Scientific American* (June 1965).

Irving, L. "Adaptations to Cold," *Scientific American* (January 1966).

Levine, R. and M. S. Goldstein. "The Action of Insulin," *Scientific American*. (May 1955).

Scholander, P. F. "The Wonderful Net," *Scientific American* (April 1957).

Tepperman, J. *Metabolic and Endocrine Physiology*. Chicago: Yearbook Medical Publishers, Inc. 1963.

Wilkins, L. "The Thyroid Gland," *Scientific American* (March 1960).

11 INTERPRETING THE ENVIRONMENT: THE BRAIN

Fig. 11.1 Self-portrait of Leonardo da Vinci: man as a creative animal stands alone in the animal kingdom. No other organism is capable of contemplating itself in an analytical way.

Up to now we have considered how man survives by regulating his internal environment. But a significant part of man's success in surviving depends on his ability to change his external environment. This involves a large variety of behavior patterns ranging from the reflex withdrawal of a hand from a hot stove to the invention of agriculture, the use of shelter and clothing, the storage of food, and interaction with other men. All of these activities depend on the central nervous system, the brain, and spinal cord.

Suppose that you see a bunch of grapes on a table, walk over and pick one up. You see the grapes with your eyes, then use muscles in your legs and arms to get to the grapes. Nerve impulses that originate in your eye touch off a chain of events leading to the activation of many different muscles. Still other muscles would have to be activated if you were going to catch a grape tossed to you. We could imagine direct pathways (nerves) leading from the eye (and every other receptor) to every muscle in the body. If this were the case, then all motions would be possible, but the number of nerves and connections would have to be enormous; and the actions that took place would probably be chaotic. Instead, the eye and other receptors send their impulses to a central station, the brain and spinal cord. From here connections are made with nerves that lead to different muscles. This is like a telephone switchboard. Each telephone has a wire leading into the central switchboard, and if appropriate connections are made there, any telephone user can call any other user. There is no need for each telephone to have a direct line to every other telephone in the country.

The nervous system is much more than a simple switchboard. The messages (nerve impulses) sent from the central nervous system to the effectors are determined not only by the incoming messages from all parts of the body, but also by the past history of incoming messages. In other words, the central nervous system has a "memory;" in addition, it can learn and is capable of com-

126

bining in unique ways the information it gathers. The result of such gathering and storage of information may give rise to a work of art, a scientific theory, or a "nervous breakdown." Today we have very little understanding of these higher mental activities, and we are only beginning to appreciate some of the simpler forms of behavior.

DEVELOPMENT AND STRUCTURE OF THE CNS

The central nervous system of an adult human being is an extremely complex structure, yet it begins as a simple line of cells on the back of the developing embryo. The cells that form the line begin to divide, then form a groove which later develops into a hollow tube, the **neural tube** (Fig. 11.2). The brain and spinal cord develop out of this primitive neural tube. At the head end of the embryo, the brain develops from three bulging structures, the **forebrain,** the **midbrain,** and the **hindbrain** (Fig. 11.2). The remaining portion of the neural tube becomes the spinal cord. Portions of the forebrain and hindbrain greatly increase in size and give rise to two very prominent structures of the adult brain—the **cerebrum** and the **cerebellum** (Fig. 11.2). Both of these structures are covered by an outer layer of cells which gives them a gray color. This outer gray layer is called the **cortex.**

The brain develops from a hollow tubular structure. In the adult the hollow interior persists in the form of an intricate system of chambers (or **ventricles**) which contain the **cerebrospinal fluid.**

In the human, the cerebrum is the most massive part of the brain and is divided into two hemispheres. The cerebral cortex grows so large that it folds in on itself in wrinkles and is thus contained in the available space within the skull. When you look down on an open skull the exposed part of the brain consists primarily of the wrinkled cortex, looking something like a large, soft walnut.

Most of the mental abilities that set man apart from other animals are thought to be due to his more highly developed cortex. If a man loses his cortex he becomes an absolute idiot. On the other hand, however, a frog is not nearly so dependent on its cerebral cortex. Even if the animal loses its cortex it may be difficult to distinguish the frog from a normal frog. Apparently the primitive behavior characteristic of a normal frog can be carried out to a large extent by structures lying beneath the cortex.

Nerve fibers carrying impulses to and from the cells of the

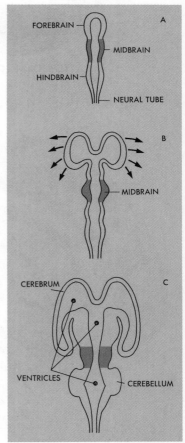

Drawn after E. D. Gardner "Fundamentals of Neurology," W. B. Saunders Co.

Fig. 11.2 The nervous system develops from a hollow tube (A). At the head-end of the tube three bulging structures become prominent and develop into the brain (B and C).

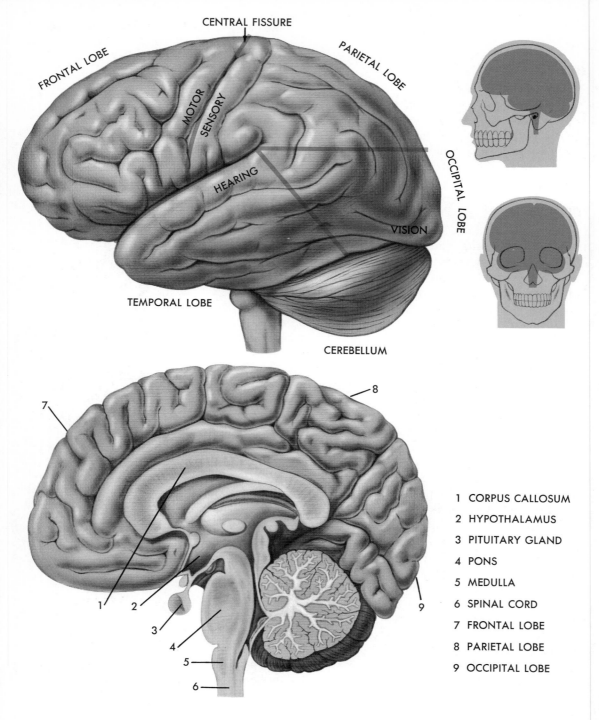

CENTRAL FISSURE

FRONTAL LOBE

PARIETAL LOBE

MOTOR

SENSORY

OCCIPITAL LOBE

HEARING

VISION

TEMPORAL LOBE

CEREBELLUM

7

8

1 CORPUS CALLOSUM

2 HYPOTHALAMUS

3 PITUITARY GLAND

4 PONS

5 MEDULLA

6 SPINAL CORD

7 FRONTAL LOBE

8 PARIETAL LOBE

9 OCCIPITAL LOBE

1

2

3

4

5

6

9

THE HUMAN BRAIN

Fig. 11.3   Man's brain is the single organ that most sets him apart from all other organisms. The highly developed cerebrum has a surface consisting of many folds, which increase its area. On the scale of evolution, the cerebral cortex, which forms a thin layer over the cerebrum, is a relatively new refinement. We are just now beginning to learn something about its role in determining our behavior and how it interacts with other parts of the brain. The bottom illustration shows a longitudinal cut through the brain, exposing the inner surface of the right hemisphere.

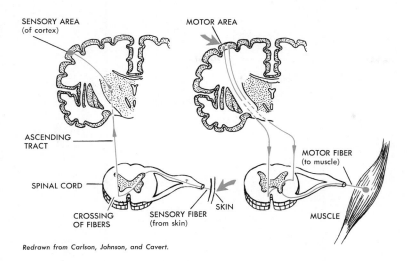

SENSORY AREA
(of cortex)

MOTOR AREA

ASCENDING
TRACT

SPINAL CORD

CROSSING
OF FIBERS

SENSORY FIBER
(from skin)

SKIN

MOTOR FIBER
(to muscle)

MUSCLE

Fig. 11.4 At left, skin is stimulated on the left side of the body. An impulse travels to the right side of the brain, where it arrives in the sensory area of the cortex. At right, a motor impulse leaves the motor area of the cortex on the right-hand side of the brain and travels to a muscle on the left side of the body.

Redrawn from Carlson, Johnson, and Cavert.

gray cortex make connections only with other cells of the brain and spinal cord. These cells, in turn, may be connected to the receptors or muscles and glands in the body. The more developed the cortex, the more it seems to overshadow and dominate these deeper brain and spinal cord structures.

Mapping the Cortex

We can begin studying the brain by stimulating different parts of the cortex. If we choose a certain area and stimulate it, a specific movement is produced. For example, stimulating one small spot makes a finger move; if an adjacent area is stimulated the whole arm may move. These areas, called **motor areas,** have been discovered during experiments with animals and during brain operations on humans. The motor areas are clustered in the region (indicated in Fig. 11.3) just in front of a prominent groove known as the **central fissure.** Just about any part of the body can be made to move if we stimulate some spot within this area (Fig. 11.5). Stimulating the motor areas on the left cerebral hemisphere always causes movements on the right side of the body; similarly, stimulating the right motor cortex produces movements on the left side. This also seems to be true for many other brain activities. The left side of the brain controls the right side of the body; the right side of the brain controls the left side of the body (Fig. 11.4).

The size of the brain controlling a particular part of the body is not related to the size of the body part; instead, it seems to be proportional to the skill or complexity of movement of which that body part is capable. The cortical areas devoted to finger

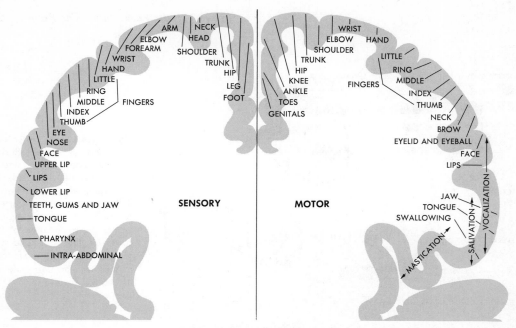

ARM NECK
ELBOW HEAD
FOREARM SHOULDER
WRIST TRUNK
HAND HIP
LITTLE LEG
RING FOOT
MIDDLE FINGERS
INDEX
THUMB
EYE
NOSE
FACE
UPPER LIP
LIPS
LOWER LIP
TEETH, GUMS AND JAW
TONGUE
PHARYNX
INTRA-ABDOMINAL

WRIST
ELBOW HAND
SHOULDER
TRUNK LITTLE
HIP RING
KNEE MIDDLE
ANKLE FINGERS INDEX
TOES THUMB
GENITALS NECK
BROW
EYELID AND EYEBALL
FACE
LIPS
JAW
TONGUE
SWALLOWING
MASTICATION
SALIVATION
VOCALIZATION

SENSORY   MOTOR

Fig. 11.5 These diagrams show certain brain areas that are associated with various activities. The sensory cortex shown here is located just behind the central fissure; the motor cortex is just in front.

Redrawn from Scientific American.

movements, for example, are much larger than areas devoted to movements of muscles in the back.

If we move our stimulating electrodes backwards from the motor area to the area labeled "sensory" in Fig. 11.3, we find that movements are no longer produced; instead, tingling sensations are felt. These sensations are not felt on the brain but in specific parts of the body such as the fingertips or face. Apparently, sensations coming from different parts of the body are sent to specific regions on the sensory cortex. We can verify this by another type of experiment. If we stimulate different parts of the body with bristles of a stiff brush we find that there is an increase in electrical activity in the sensory cortex. When we stimulate an area on the right side of the body the sensory cortex on the left cerebral hemisphere shows increased activity and *vice versa*. There is some sensory information, however, that is not directed to this part of the cortex. Vision, hearing, smell, and taste all have special cortex areas that receive incoming impulses.

Association Areas

So far, we have described those areas of the brain where sensory information arrives in the cortex, and other areas where motor commands leave. These areas occupy only a small fraction of the total cortex. The remaining areas making up the greater mass of the cortex are loosely referred to as **association areas.** The space taken up by association areas in man is relatively larger than it is in lower animals. Both men and lower animals seem to receive similar types of information from their environments. They both perform similar movements and have comparable sensory and motor areas of their brains. Nevertheless,

130

man is the superior animal because of his ability to store vast amounts of information and use it in an endless variety of combinations whenever he wishes. His ability to think reflectively seems to involve the association areas. Without these areas it would be impossible for your brain to be wondering how it works.

Let's return to our bunch of grapes on the table to illustrate the role of association areas. First you see the grapes. The image is registered on your retina, which is the light-sensitive portion of your eye, and is transmitted by the optic nerves to the brain and finally to the visual area of your cerebral cortex. However, you have yet to *recognize* what you see as grapes, and here is where the association areas play a role. The concept "grape" implies many things—for example, certain colors, texture, size, shape, taste, and smell. You gain information and form your own idea of what a grape is through many different sensations. Impulses that convey these different sensations arrive at different areas of the cortex. Yet all of this information must be integrated into a single concept, "grape." Somehow or other, association areas seem to be involved in this integration process. We get some idea of their importance by considering what happens when they are injured.

If some of the association area near the visual region of the cortex were destroyed, you would see the grapes, but you would not be able to identify them as grapes. The visual clues you would be receiving would no longer be meaningful. However, if you handled the grapes, or tasted one, or used any other sense whose association areas were still intact, you would be able to identify the objects as grapes. The association areas in some way relate sensory clues to stored (memory) information. Patients whose visual association area has been damaged have been shown keys, for example. They shook their heads, unable to recognize the objects as anything in particular. When the keys were rattled, however, the patients were able to identify them immediately.

The perception-recognition process is an extremely complex one. It not only involves what is sensed at the moment, it also involves memory of past associations and our response to them. We can imagine a mentally ill person who, upon being shown a key, reacts violently because of some unpleasant event the key causes the patient to recall. We can also imagine the response of a person who has never seen a key before. Essentially the same process of sensing and recognizing is operating in each person, but the visual association areas of the cortex along with other parts of the brain cause the two people to respond to the key stimulus in entirely different ways.

Fig. 11.6 The *cerebellum* enables us to operate with precision and with smooth coordination.

The Cerebellum

Now suppose that you pick up the grapes with a smooth, swift, motion. The accuracy of your arm motion is aided by the sight of your hand during its journey, also by sensations arising from your muscles, tendons, and joints. The cerebellum coordinates this information and plays an important role in producing smooth, accurate motion. If your cerebellum were damaged and you sat quietly, your handicap would not be noticed. But the moment you moved, your condition would be obvious. Your motion would be jerky and uncoordinated. When you reached out for the grapes your hand might overshoot them. If you attempted to correct this and bring your hand back, you might over correct and withdraw your hand too far. The result would be a series of jerky motions which eventually would "zero in" on the target.

The cerebellum seems to be involved in assessing the body's position in space and in sending out signals that enable you to make rapid corrections of faulty motions. The cerebellum receives information from the cerebral cortex, from sensory organs, and from deep sensations coming from receptors in muscles, tendons, and joints. This deep sense, called **proprioception,** provides information about the position and performance of the limbs and body. Whenever the motor cortex commands muscles to move, it sends information at the same time to the cerebellum. The cerebellum, in turn, sends impulses back to the cerebral cortex (and to other motor centers in the brain) correcting any errors with the outcome that the resulting motion is smooth and well-timed. The cerebellum is able to do this on the basis of information it is always receiving from muscles and joints; that is, it compares the "commands" of the motor cortex with the "performance" of the muscles. The cerebellum does not initiate movements. It acts only to make them precise in time and space.

Our description of the cerebellum illustrates how the cerebral cortex interacts with, and is influenced by, other parts of the brain. Even the simplest behavior patterns are not wrapped up in neat little anatomical packages in the brain, where we can stimulate them or cut them out. The dependence of the cerebral cortex on deeper brain structures is further emphasized in the process of sleep and attention.

Sleep and Attention: the Reticular Formation

The possibility of awakening from sleep and remaining conscious seems to depend on a diffuse network of nerve cells called the **reticular formation** (Fig. 11.7). Stimulation of one part of the reticular formation awakens a sleeping animal, more or less as though it had been gently patted on the head. If the reticular formation is destroyed, the animal immediately lapses into a deep sleep, or coma, never again to awaken. The reticular formation is necessary if the awakened conscious state is to persist. We can interpret this by assuming that when the reticular formation receives sufficient sensory impulses from the environment it showers the cortex with activating impulses which are necessary to alert it.

Recent experiments suggest that lower brain centers can filter information that is passed along to the higher centers. This filtering process may be important in directing our attention to specific subjects. When you are reading, for example, and are unaware of noises around you, it *seems* as though impulses that would ordinarily convey noise sensations do not reach your cortex. Experiments on cats suggest that not only does it *seem* as though these impulses do not reach the cortex, but they *actually* may not.

In an experiment, each cat had an electrode implanted in the medulla at the point where the nerve carrying impulses from the ear first makes synaptic connections with nerve cells in the brain. From here, impulses are sent on toward the cerebral cortex. The electrode was used to record the cat's responses to noise. Whenever a clicking noise was made near the cat's ear a wave of electrical activity was received by the electrode. Each time there was a click, there was a wave of activity. Next, the cat's attention was diverted to something of special interest, such as some live mice. As soon as the cat became interested in the mice, the electrical activity produced by the continuing series of clicks decreased. The cat no longer "heard" the clicks because nerve impulses from the ear were not reaching the cortex. Apparently the lower parts of the brain, and in some cases the receptors, are capable of filtering information before it is passed on to the cortex.

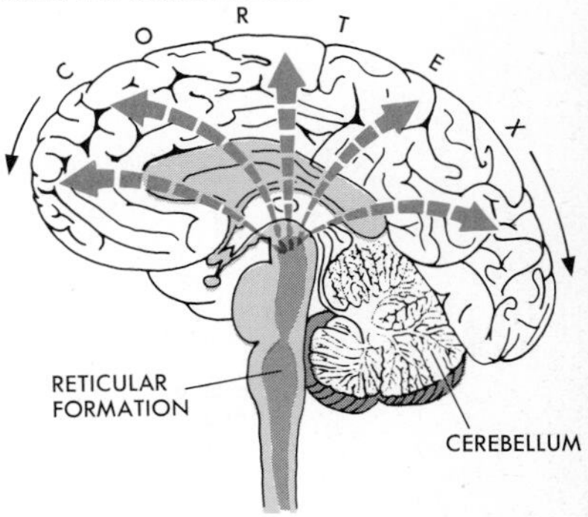

Memory

The human brain has the remarkable capacity of storing impressions of the past and calling them into consciousness at appropriate times. Are there specific memory areas in the brain? And what physical changes take place as a result of this storage of information? Here again our information is meager; the best we can do is offer some of the observations and experiments which may provide clues.

Fig. 11.7 The *reticular formation* receives sensory impulses from the environment and showers the cortex with activating impulses, thus alerting it.

Drawn after Scientific American

RETICULAR FORMATION

CEREBELLUM

Some of our memories are fleeting, yet others endure. After recovering from a blow on the head a person may suffer from loss of memory, but as time passes he regains his memory. However, he may never remember what happened just a few moments before the blow was struck. It seems that a certain length of time is needed for an event to be transferred to our permanent memory. This can be shown very clearly in laboratory animals. Say that we train an animal to perform a certain task and within five minutes after each training session we give the animal a severe electric shock. The animal then shows no signs of remembering what it was taught during the session. However, if the animal is given a shock several hours after each training session, the shock has no effect on its training; that is, it learns to perform the task and remembers what it has learned just as well as animals which are not given a shock.

What do these experiments suggest about the processes involved in the storage of information? Possibly there are two stages: first, as soon as information—a new telephone number, say—reaches the brain it is stored, but only temporarily. Sometime later, and this would be the second stage, the information is more permanently stored. If an electrical shock, or a blow on the head is delivered during the first stage, the information is lost so that when the brain recovers, the information cannot be processed and delivered to a permanent memory storage. Some scientists now think that the permanent memory mechanism may ultimately be traced to chemical changes in some of the structures of the nerve cells, and that the process of information storage in the nervous system is related to protein synthesis. It should be emphasized, however, that we still have very little evidence to construct a theory of memory, so these last remarks can be considered only a guess about what may be revealed in the future.

Perhaps the most startling discovery made about memory is that the brain can be stimulated to recall events long past. Some of the first comprehensive reports of this phenomenon came from Wilder Penfield, a neurosurgeon in Montreal. Penfield was interested in the surgical removal of diseased parts of the brain, and he wanted to be sure that he did not remove any brain part that was vital to normal activities, such as speech. His technique was to expose the surface of the brain under local anesthesia. Even though the patient was fully conscious, the exposed brain caused no discomfort because there are no pain receptors on the surface. Penfield would then stimulate different parts of the brain with electrodes. Next he would ask the patient what he felt and would observe any motions. In this way he could associate the patient's response with certain brain areas stimulated and then carefully select the diseased areas which could be removed safely. By recording all of his observations Penfield made significant contributions to our knowledge of the localization of functions in the human brain.

During the course of one of these operations an electrode was applied to the grey matter on the face of one of the temporal lobes (see Fig. 11.3). Here is how Penfield described what happened:

". . . the patient observed: 'I hear some music.' Fifteen minutes later, the electrode was applied to the same spot again without her knowledge. 'I hear music again,' she said. 'It is like radio.' Again and again, then, the electrode tip was applied to this point. Each time, she heard an orchestra playing the same piece of music. . . . Seeing the electrical stimulator box, from where she lay under the surgical coverings, she thought it was a gramophone that someone was turning on from time to time. She was asked to describe the music. When the electrode was applied again, she began to hum a tune, and all in the operating room listened in astonished silence. She was obviously humming along with the orchestra at about the tempo that would be expected. . . .

"After the patient returned home, she wrote to me on April 16, 1950. The letter was, in part, as follows: . . . 'I heard the song right from the beginning and you know I could remember much more of it right in the operating room. . . . There were instruments . . . . It was as though it were being played by an orchestra. Definitely it was *not* as though I were imagining the tune to myself. I actually heard it. It is not one of my favorite songs, so I don't know why I heard that song.'"

[After similar observations Penfield concludes] ". . . that there is, hidden away in the brain, a record of the stream of consciousness. It seems to hold the detail of that stream as laid down during each man's waking conscious hours. Contained in this record are all those things of which the individual was once aware—such detail as a man might hope to remember for a few seconds or minutes afterwards, but which are largely lost to voluntary recall after that time. The things that he ignored are absent from the record." [From: *Proceedings of the National Academy of Science,* Volume 44, 1958, page 57.]

Conditioned Reflex

The process of learning is a good example of how stored information is put to use. One of the most primitive types of learning, called **conditioned reflex,** was studied by the Russian physiologist Ivan Pavlov. Pavlov knew that whenever he placed meat in the mouth of a dog the animal would reflexly salivate; in other words, its mouth would "water" automatically. He experimented with this reflex in dogs by ringing a bell each time he gave meat to the dog. After many trials, Pavlov found that if he withheld the meat and simply rang the bell the dog would still salivate. The dog had been **conditioned** to associate the sound of the bell with the presence of meat in his mouth.

The flow of saliva that usually follows the sight of meat is in itself a conditioned reflex. Pavlov proved this by raising puppies without ever giving them meat. When the puppies were shown meat, they did not salivate. However, after the meat had been placed in their mouth a few times, they began to salivate whenever they saw meat.

It is possible to combine different types of stimuli into conditioned reflexes in novel ways. Normally you cannot voluntarily control the size of the pupil in your eye, but if a bright light shines in your eye, the pupil will automatically (reflexly) constrict. If someone rings a bell each time the light is turned on you may become conditioned to the sound of the bell. Now you have some control. Each time you ring the bell, your pupil will constrict, even though the light is not on.

Conditioned reflexes are a useful tool to study animal behavior. Dogs, for example, can be conditioned to distinguish between different shades of grey, but not between different colors. From this we infer that dogs are color blind. Interesting behavior in animals results when they are forced to make difficult discriminations. A dog can be conditioned to salivate whenever he sees a circle, but not to salivate when an ellipse appears. Now, the ellipse is made more and more circular until the dog is not able to tell the difference between the ellipse and the circle. At this point the dog begins to show signs of anxiety, squealing and wiggling about. He may whine and howl and have violent temper tantrums—he becomes "neurotic."

The conditioned reflexes we have described thus far may not be of any particular advantage to the animal. The response is fully automatic and not under voluntary control. More complicated and useful forms of learning occur when an animal is punished or rewarded for responses that are under voluntary control. An animal may be placed in a situation where he must choose between two alternatives, say, turning to the right or turning to the left. By turning to the right he is rewarded; by turning to the left he is punished. Here, the voluntary action of turning to the right and the reward are associated. In short, the animal is taught to perform some task, or to operate within the environment, in order to obtain a reward or avoid punishment.

The physical or neuronal basis for even primitive learning such as conditioning is not known. A search for specific areas on the cortex which might be involved in learning has not been fruitful. Rather than finding specific "learning" areas, the whole brain seems to be involved. This problem has been studied extensively in white rats. Different parts of the cortex have been removed to find out what, if any, effect the surgery would have on the amount of practice required to learn to run a maze. No matter what part of the cortex was removed, the learning process was slowed. The size of the piece of cortex removed seemed to be more important than the area from which it was taken.

The only information that reaches our brain is sent there by our sensory receptors. Let us now turn to two of man's most important special senses—sight and hearing.

HEARING AND THE EAR

Think of the variety of sounds you hear during just about any five-minute period of a typical day: loud noise and soft noise, high-pitched tones and low-pitched tones. Among the many aspects of hearing that physiologists study, two have been particularly interesting: 1. how the ear translates sound into action potentials along the sensory nerve which leads to the brain; and 2. how high-pitched tones are discriminated from low-pitched tones.

The sound a book makes when you drop it onto a table is a complex one because it consists of many different pitches. Simpler sounds, pure tones, can be produced by hitting a tuning fork so that the tines vibrate. As each tine moves outward, it compresses the air in front of it. The region of compressed air in front of the tine tends to compress the air just adjacent to it, and this new region of compressed air also tends to compress adjacent air (Fig. 11.8). In this way the area of compression travels outward in all directions from the tine of the fork, at 1129 feet per second (770 miles per hour). Since the fork is vibrating, this means that it is moving forward many times per second and producing many waves of compression, which constitute **sound waves.**

Now suppose that we put a membrane in the path of these sound waves. As each wave of compressed air hits the membrane it pushes against the membrane, and stretches it. Each time a wave of compressed air hits the membrane, the same thing happens. The membrane vibrates. The **tympanum,** or ear drum (Fig. 11.9), is just such a membrane that initiates a series of events leading to our perception of sound. When the strength of the vibration is increased, we hear a louder sound. When the frequency of vibrations (the number of them per second) is increased, the pitch becomes higher. The human ear can hear between about 20 and 20,000 vibrations (cycles) per second. Middle C corresponds to 256 c.p.s.

The tympanum separates the external ear from the middle ear (Fig. 11.9). The external and middle ear are filled with air; the inner ear is filled with fluid. The coiled portion of the inner

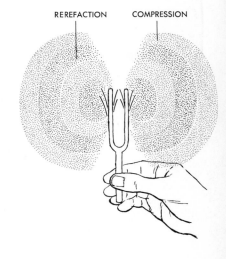

Fig. 11.8 Areas of compressed air travel outward as waves from the tines of a tuning fork. The ear and brain perceive the waves as sound.

REREFACTION   COMPRESSION

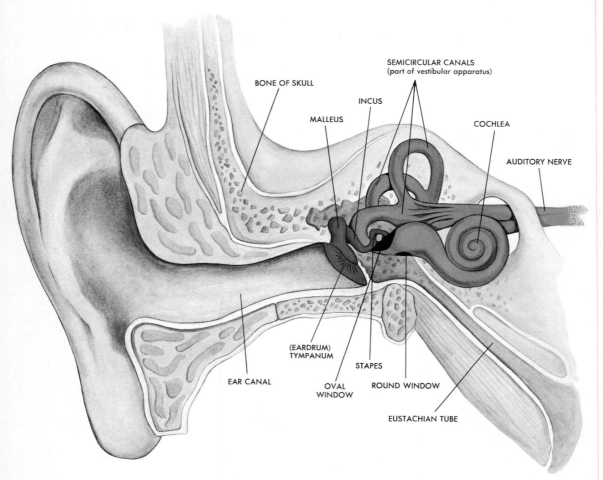

BONE OF SKULL

SEMICIRCULAR CANALS
(part of vestibular apparatus)

INCUS

MALLEUS

COCHLEA

AUDITORY NERVE

(EARDRUM)
TYMPANUM

STAPES

EAR CANAL

OVAL
WINDOW

ROUND WINDOW

EUSTACHIAN TUBE

Fig. 11.9 This diagram shows the various parts of the outer, middle, and inner ear.

ear, called the **cochlea,** is very important for hearing. The fluid-filled cochlea is divided into three major compartments by two flexible membranes. One of them—the basilar membrane—connects with nerve endings that transmit impulses from the ear to the brain.

The middle and inner ear are separated by rigid walls except at two places, the oval window and the round window, as shown in Fig. 11.10. Here the separating walls consist of membranous material which can stretch. The bones of the middle ear form a bridge between the ear drum and the oval window. If we were able to take hold of the ear drum and move it back and forth the bones would also move back and forth, and since they are connected to the oval window it, too, would move back and forth. Because the inner ear is filled with fluid, every time the oval window is pushed in, the round window bulges outward. That is, the fluid in the inner ear pulsates with the ear drum.

The membranes separating the compartments of the inner ear are pliable. When the fluid vibrates, these membranes also vibrate and move up and down. These movements of the basilar membrane are responsible for stimulation of the nerve endings.

If we follow a compression wave from the moment the oval window is pushed in, we find an important clue to how the ear discriminates pitch. The wave of compression does not necessarily go all the way down to the end of the inner ear, bounce off the wall and then back on the other side to the round window (broken line in Fig. 11.10). Rather it tends to take a shorter path and goes through the basilar membrane (solid line in Fig. 11.10). This means that some parts of the basilar membrane will move and be deformed more than others. With low frequencies the wave tends to travel farther on down before it turns and goes through the basilar membrane. With high frequencies (more rapid vibrations) a shorter path is taken and the maximum deformation occurs closer and closer to the middle ear. This is the basis for pitch discrimination. For each frequency there is a particular part of the basilar membrane that vibrates most strongly. When the nerve impulses from that region dominate we get the characteristic sensation of that particular pitch. Thus when most of the impulses come from a specific region of the basilar membrane, they give you the sensation of hearing, say, middle C. A pitch higher than middle C would come from nerve fibers located closer to the middle ear, and likewise a pitch lower than middle C would come from nerve fibers located farther away.

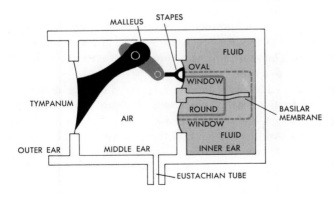

Fig. 11.10 A wave of compression transmitted by the ear drum does not travel all the way to the end of the inner ear (dotted line). Instead, it tends to take a shorter path, passing through the basilar membrane (solid line).

Our evidence for this theory of pitch discrimination comes from several sources. Some people are deaf only to specific tones. Autopsy shows that in such people specific regions of the basilar membrane had been injured. These sites correspond to the sites which we would predict on the basis of the theory. Second, we can produce lesions in laboratory animals by exposing them to loud noises. By selecting a particular pitch, and subjecting the animal to an intense sound of that pitch, we can cause a particular part of the basilar membrane to vibrate so violently that it becomes damaged. These animals will then be deaf to that pitch. (How would you test this in an animal?)

As Fig. 11.9 or 11.10 shows, the air in the middle ear is not sealed off from the air surrounding it. A tube called the **eustachian tube** leads from the middle ear to the mouth. This opening is very important in preventing the development of any pressure differences across the ear drum. If a large pressure difference did develop, the ear drum could shatter. For example, when you climb a mountain the air around you becomes less and less dense. If there were no eustachian tube, the pressure in the middle ear would remain at its sea-level value. Pressure in the middle ear, then, would be greater than in the external ear. This would cause the ear drum to bulge outward. If the pressure difference became great enough, the ear drum would break. The sensation you notice when you take off or land in an airplane is due to mild pressure differences before your ears are adjusted by the eustachian tube. Sometimes you can help their adjustment by yawning, which helps clear the opening of the eustachian tube.

In Fig. 11.9 you may have noticed structures in the inner ear which we have not considered. These make up the **vestibular apparatus.** They are not concerned at all with hearing, but enable you to detect the motion of your head and thus orient yourself in space. The inner ear, then, consists of two organs, the cochlear part, which is concerned with hearing, and the vestibular apparatus which is concerned with motion and orientation.

SEEING AND THE EYE

A number of problems concerned with vision are resolved in the eye—focusing, seeing in bright or dim light, and so on. The main problem is how light energy is transformed into action potentials.

As Fig. 11.11 shows, the eye is covered on the outside with a tough white tissue called the **sclera.** Toward the front of the eye, where it bulges, the sclera becomes transparent and is known as the **cornea.** An inner layer, called the **retina,** contains cells sensitive to light. These cells are connected to nerve fibers that transmit impulses to the brain. If the eye were a camera, the retina would correspond to the film.

As you can see from Fig. 11.11, the eye lens divides the eye into two chambers, both of which are filled with fluid. Like a lens on a camera, the lens of the eye must be brought into focus if the eye is to get a sharp image of what we are looking at. In

140

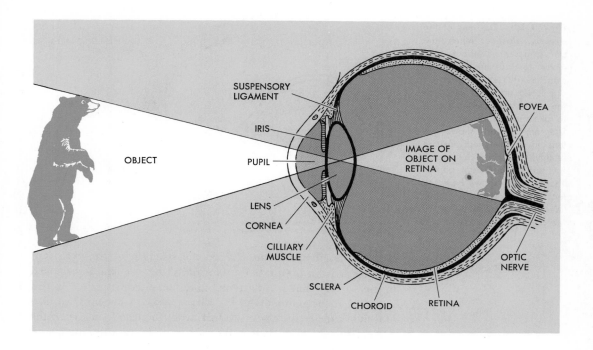

SUSPENSORY
LIGAMENT

IRIS

OBJECT

PUPIL

LENS

CORNEA

CILLIARY
MUSCLE

SCLERA

CHOROID

RETINA

IMAGE OF
OBJECT ON
RETINA

FOVEA

OPTIC
NERVE

Fig. 11.11 The human eye
and a camera are similar in
many respects.

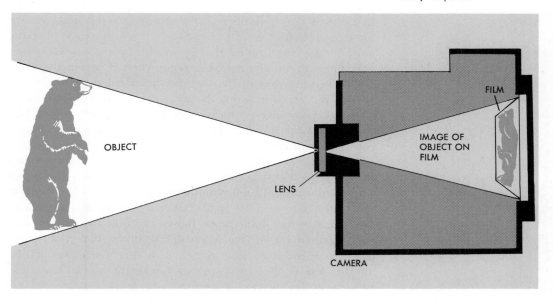

OBJECT

FILM

IMAGE OF
OBJECT ON
FILM

LENS

CAMERA

Fig. 11.12 The lens of the eye is elastic. When the *ciliary* muscles contract, they move toward the point of attachment (see diagram at right), relaxing the tension on the lens and permitting it to take a more rounded shape. Diagram at left shows the lens in a stretched position (solid line), when the eye is focused on a distant object. The red line shows how the lens *accommodates* and thus keeps an object in focus as the object moves closer.

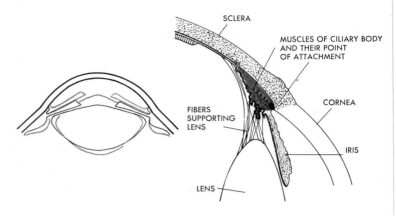

Drawn after Winton and Bayliss, Human Physiology, Little Brown.
Drawn after Carlson, Johnson, and Cavert, Machinery of the Body.

order to do this, we can change the strength of the eye's lens because it is an elastic body. Normally the eye lens is stretched in such a way that it is flattened and elongated. It is held in this shape by its attachments to the **ciliary body.** A person with normal eyes can see an object 20 feet away in clear focus when the ciliary muscles are relaxed. But if the object is brought closer, and the ciliary muscles remain relaxed, the object becomes blurred. For the object to be kept in focus, your ciliary muscles must contract, in the process pulling the lens attachments closer together and thereby releasing tension on the lens. This action permits the lens to get rounder and more powerful (Fig. 11.12). In this way you are able to get sharp images of objects as they are moved as close as $3\frac{1}{2}$ inches away from your eye. Try looking at your finger and notice that as you bring it closer and closer your finger eventually reaches a point where it becomes blurred. This is because your eye lens has become as round as it can get.

This process of adjusting the eyes so that they can focus on an object as it is brought closer is called **accommodation.** In addition to changing the shape of the lens, accommodation also causes a constriction of the pupil (the opening of the eye which permits light to enter and reach the retina) and a change in the position of the eye so that it begins to point toward the nose. The power of accommodation usually diminishes with age. This is because the lenses become more rigid, hence it is difficult for them to take on a round shape when the ciliary muscles contract and reduce tension on the lens. Many defects in the lens system of the eye can be corrected with glasses. This simply involves adding another lens to the system, just as you might add an extra lens to a camera to increase its performance.

A good photographer is not only concerned with the lens system in his camera, but also is careful in selecting his film. In bright sunlight he uses a relatively insensitive film, which he replaces with a sensitive film for dimly lit subjects. The eye employs the same strategy by using different cells of the retina. The retina has two types of light-sensitive cells. One type consists of **rods,** the other of **cones.** We can illustrate the functions of the rods and cones by some simple examples. If you want to see fine detail in the daytime it is best to look directly at the object. By doing so, you are causing light reflected from the object to fall on the central part of your retina, the **fovea.** At night the situation is quite different. On entering a dark room it is best not to look *directly* at an object. If you want to see it more clearly, look at it out of the side of your eye, so that light reflected from the object falls toward the edges of the retina (Fig. 11.13). When we compare the distribution of the rod cells and the cone cells in the retina, we find that the cones are most concentrated toward the center and the rods toward the edges. This leads us to believe that the cones are primarily concerned with day vision and the rods are mostly concerned with night vision. This is confirmed when we study animals that have poor vision in the dark and contrast them with animals, like bats or owls, which see very well at night. Animals with little or no night vision have retinas containing mostly cones. Bats, owls, and other animals with good night vision have more rods in their retinas.

What happens in the cones and the rods when light falls on them? Our information is not complete in either case, but we do know more about rods than cones. The rods contain a pigment called **visual purple.** When light falls on visual purple the visual purple is bleached. During the bleaching process action potentials are set up on the nerve fibers connected to the rod cells. It is at this point that light energy is in some way translated into action potentials. When you are in a bright room, there is little visual purple in the rods, so your rods are ineffective. This is because the visual purple has been bleached by the bright light. Now if you go into a dark room, your rods are of little use to you immediately; but if you wait a few minutes, visual purple will be regenerated and will enable your rod cells to function. Gradually you will see objects in the room more and more clearly. Now suppose that you have become completely adapted to the dark and suddenly go into the light. At this point the light "hurts" your eyes and you have difficulty seeing. Now your rod cells, with a full supply of visual purple, are too effective. They are so effective that *everything* looks very bright; there is no contrast. You have to remain in the light a few minutes until the visual purple has been bleached so that the highly sensitive rods no longer respond. Information originating in the cones is then no longer "swamped" by the great activity of the rods.

Fig. 11.13 In a dark room it is easier to see objects if you don't look directly at them. The object at B is easier to see if you look directly at Point A. Light from the object at B will then fall on a region of the retina rich in rods.

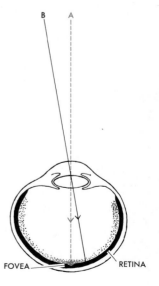

SUMMARY

The **cerebrum** is the most massive part of the brain. Its gray surface, or **cortex,** is particularly well developed in man and it is essential for man's unique mental abilities. Although parts of the brain involved in various physiological functions have been located, attempts to localize complex behavior patterns in areas have failed. The cerebral cortex interacts with itself and with other parts of the brain in a complex way. Our present efforts to describe these interactions are at an early stage of development.

Sensory areas, where impulses first arrive on the cortex, have been located. **Motor areas,** where "command" impulses leave the cortex, have also been located. Other areas of the cortex are thought to be involved in *associations* of sensory information. Stimulating some parts of the cortex produces a detailed recall of past events.

The **cerebellum** receives impulses from sensory receptors and interacts with the motor cortex, insuring smooth muscular movements. Damage to the cerebellum results in a loss of coordination. The **reticular formation** receives sensory impulses from the environment and sends impulses to the cortex. If this part of the brain is destroyed, the animal will sleep and never awaken.

The ear has three parts—the **external ear,** the **middle ear,** and the **inner ear.** Vibrations caused by sound waves striking the tympanum are transmitted (by the bones of the middle ear) to the oval window of the cochlea, then through the fluid of the cochlea to the basilar membrane. Deformations in the basilar membrane stimulate sensory nerve endings, which transmit impulses to the brain. The pattern of vibrations of the basilar membrane depends on the frequency of sound waves. This provides a basis for pitch discrimination.

The light-sensitive portion of the eye is called the **retina.** Light reflected from objects is focused on the retina by the lens. The retina is composed of **rods** (most numerous toward the periphery of the retina) and **cones** (most numerous at the center of the retina). Cones are stimulated by bright light (day vision); the rods are stimulated by dim light (night vision). Rods contain a pigment, **visual purple,** which is bleached by light. During the bleaching process, action potentials are set up on nerve fibers which carry impulses to the brain.

FOR THOUGHT AND DISCUSSION

1 When you take an examination, you read a question, pick up a pencil, and begin writing. Your performance depends on

sensory receptors, nerves, the central nervous system, and muscles. Outline the interactions that take place between your eyes, brain, and muscles in your arm.

2 When you first enter a movie theater, it is difficult to find your way to an empty seat. However, after a short time your vision improves (explain) and you can see the person in the next seat in detail; but can you distinguish the color of his clothing? What does this suggest about the ability of rods and cones to discriminate colors?

3 What handicaps would result from: (a) Damage to the cerebellum? (b) Damage to the peripheral parts of the retina? (c) A clogged eustachian tube? (d) Damage to a small portion of the basilar membrane lying close to the oval window? (e) Damage to the motor areas on the cortex of the right cerebral hemisphere? (f) Damage to sensory areas on the cortex of the left cerebral hemisphere? Would either or both of the last two injuries [cases (e) or (f)] interfere with the withdrawal of a hand from a hot stove? Explain.

SELECTED READINGS

French, J. D. "The Reticular Formation," *Scientific American* (May 1957) (reprint #66).

Grey, W. W. "The Electrical Activity of the Brain," *Scientific American* (June 1954) (reprint #73).

Hubel, D. H. "The Visual Cortex of the Brain," *Scientific American* (November 1963) (reprint #168).

McGaugh, J. L., Weinberger, N. M., and Whalen, R. E. *Psychobiology— Readings from Scientific American.* San Francisco: W. H. Freeman and Co., 1967.

Olds, J. "Pleasure Centers in the Brain," *Scientific American* (October 1956) (reprint #30).

Rushton, W. A. H. "Visual Pigments in Man," *Scientific American* (November 1962) (reprint #139).

Snider, R. S. "The Cerebellum," *Scientific American* (August 1958) (reprint #38).

Sperry, R. W. "The Great Cerebral Commissure," *Scientific American* (January 1964) (reprint #174).

von Bekesy, G. "The Ear," *Scientific American* (August, 1957) (reprint #44).

Wald, G. "Eye and Camera," *Scientific American* (August 1950) (reprint #46).

Woolderidge, D. E. *Machinery of the Brain.* New York: McGraw-Hill, 1963.

12 REPRODUCTION

Throughout this book we have emphasized problems related to the physical survival of an individual man. We have seen many examples of delicately balanced regulatory devices that protect the environment of living cells, enabling them to flourish. Nevertheless, eventually each man dies, and it is our ability to reproduce that sustains the life process of our species.

In man, as well as in other animals and plants, reproduction involves the division of cells. Hereditary material (contained in chromosomes) which directs cellular activities is replicated and distributed in such a way that each cell receives an identical complement. In some primitive organisms new individuals sometimes arise by a simple process of duplication—a single cell divides into two individuals. However, in most species of plants and animals, including man, new individuals arise only out of the union of two separate individuals; that is, through sexual reproduction.

Fig. 12.1 Of the millions of sperm cells that surround an ovum only one penetrates and fertilizes the egg cell.

Courtesy L. R. Shettles, Ovum Humalium, Hafner Publishing Co.

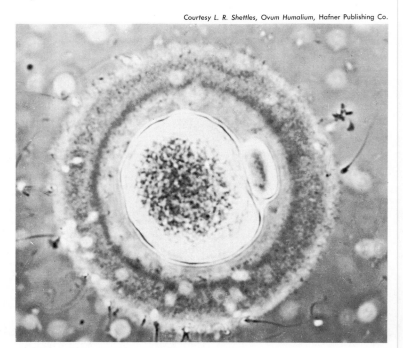

The Biological Significance of Sexual Reproduction

The development of each living organism follows a "blueprint" (determined by genes) inherited from its parents. If reproduction required only one parent then the offspring would inherit one set of genes and would resemble his parent in every detail. In sexual reproduction, however, each new individual inherits two sets of genes, one from each parent. He is different from both parents, having inherited some traits from one and certain traits from the other. This raises the possibility that some of the offspring may be stronger than either parent, and better able to survive. It does not necessarily follow that the offspring *will* be stronger than either of his parents, but at least the possibility is open.

One advantage of sexual reproduction is that it produces variety. Within any given species each individual differs from all others. Some may be small and fast, others large and sluggish, and still others may be more intelligent. Without knowing what environmental changes are apt to occur, it is impossible to predict which are the best possible traits that would enable a species to flourish a thousand years hence. Nevertheless, for any environmental change that is not drastic, there is a good chance that at least some members of the species would have just the right traits to enable them, and the species, to survive. The chance of this occurring would be much smaller if each offspring stemmed from a single parent and was an exact replica of it.

Sexual reproduction always involves specialized cells called **gametes.** There are two types of gametes; 1. **sperm** (produced by the male) and 2. **ova,** or eggs (produced by the female). A new individual will develop only after a sperm cell has united with an ovum (one egg cell). The fusion of a sperm cell with an ovum is called **fertilization.** A newly fertilized egg contains two sets of genes, a set from each parent. Before discussing some of the problems faced by this egg, we should first find out how the formation of sperm and ova is controlled in the male and female.

PRODUCTION OF SPERM

The organs involved in the production and liberation of human sperm are illustrated in Fig. 12.2. Sperm are produced in the **testes,** which are contained in the **scrotum,** located outside of the abdominal cavity. The testes consist of thousands of small tubules which lead through a series of tubes to the urethra and to the outside. These tubules, called **seminiferous tubules,** produce the sperm. The location of the testes outside of the body in the scrotum is very important, because the develop-

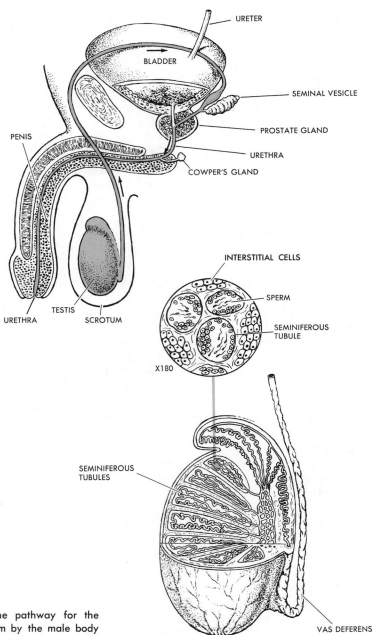

URETER

BLADDER

SEMINAL VESICLE

PROSTATE GLAND

URETHRA

COWPER'S GLAND

PENIS

URETHRA

TESTIS

SCROTUM

INTERSTITIAL CELLS

SPERM

SEMINIFEROUS TUBULE

X180

SEMINIFEROUS TUBULES

VAS DEFERENS

Fig. 12.2   The pathway for the release of sperm by the male body is shown in the top diagram. Sperm cells are produced in the *seminiferous tubules* (bottom diagram) of the testes. The production of sperm depends in part on the presence of the male hormone *testosterone*, which is supplied by the interstitial cells.

Redrawn from Illustrated Physiology by McNaught and Callander.
E. & S. Livingstone, Edinburgh

ment of healthy sperm takes place only at temperatures slightly lower than body temperature. In some abnormal cases, the testes do not descend into the scrotum but remain in the abdominal cavity. Sperm cannot be produced in such cases, and the men are sterile.

In going from the testes to the opening of the penis, the sperm cells pass through the **vas deferens** and pass by the **seminal vesicle, prostate,** and **Cowper's** glands. These glands secrete material which mixes with the sperm and is thought to provide the sperm with nourishment, to offer chemical protection, and to support swimming motions. These movements result when the tail of the sperm cell waves back and forth, propelling it along. The fluid, consisting of sperm cells mixed with the glandular secretions, is called **semen.**

Interspersed between the seminiferous tubules of the testes are a number of cells called **interstitial cells.** The interstitial cells secrete the male hormone **testosterone.** Testosterone is essential to the development of mature sex organs and for the development of sperm. It also promotes skeletal and muscular growth during adolescence and is necessary for the development of secondary sexual characteristics—for example, the deepening of the voice during the early teens and the growth of pubic hair, both of which are characteristic of masculinity. The secretion of testosterone and the normal development of sperm are in turn controlled by anterior pituitary secretions called **gonadotropic hormones.**

There is little or no testosterone secreted until some time between the ages of 12 and 16 years (the age of puberty). This is probably due to a lack of secretion of gonadotropic hormones by the pituitary gland. There is evidence that the gonadotropic hormones are stored in the pituitary up until this age but are not released. We do not know why they are suddenly released at this age, but we believe that they are controlled by the central nervous system.

Cycle of Ova Production

The female sex organs are illustrated in Fig. 12.3. They consist of the **ovaries** together with the **fallopian tubes** (oviducts), **uterus** (womb), and **vagina** (birth canal). The ovum begins to develop within the ovary. As it matures, it migrates toward the surface and becomes surrounded by a fluid-filled cavity called a **follicle.** Every 28 days, on the average, one of the most highly developed follicles ruptures and releases a single egg. This process is called **ovulation.** The liberated ovum then enters the fallopian tubes and after about three to four days enters the uterus.

Following ovulation, the ruptured follicle is transformed into a new structure, called the **corpus luteum.** The corpus luteum has two possible fates. If the egg has been fertilized, the corpus luteum persists for several months. Most often, however, the egg is not fertilized, in which event the corpus luteum then degenerates in about 14 days after ovulation. The cyclic changes taking place in the ovaries are illustrated in Fig. 12.4.

Cycle of Changes in the Uterus

Cyclic changes also take place in the uterus about every 28 days. The lining of the uterus, called the **endometrium,** thickens and begins to soften (Fig. 12.5). In addition, many blood vessels and small glands which store and secrete nutrient materials develop within the endometrium. This development of the uterus prepares it to house and nourish the embryo if pregnancy occurs (if the egg is fertilized). If pregnancy does not occur, endometrium development stops when the corpus luteum begins to degenerate. At this time there is a local spasm of blood vessels, which starves the cells of the thickened portions of the endometrium for oxygen and nutrients. These cells do not survive and, as a result, the thickened portions of the endometrium become detached and are discharged along with a small amount of blood (perhaps 50–250 ml) through the vagina.

Fig. 12.3 The ovum which has developed within the ovarian follicle, is released from the surface of the ovary and migrates through the fallopian tube toward the uterus. The ruptured follicle is transformed into the corpus luteum.

Drawn after Scientific American

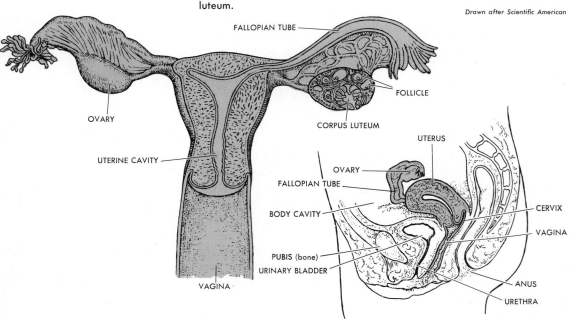

FALLOPIAN TUBE

FOLLICLE

OVARY

CORPUS LUTEUM

UTERUS

UTERINE CAVITY

OVARY

FALLOPIAN TUBE

CERVIX

BODY CAVITY

VAGINA

PUBIS (bone)

URINARY BLADDER

ANUS

VAGINA

URETHRA

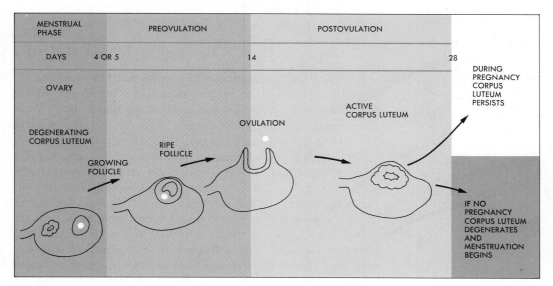

MENSTRUAL PHASE	PREOVULATION	POSTOVULATION	
DAYS 4 OR 5	14	28	DURING PREGNANCY CORPUS LUTEUM PERSISTS

OVARY

ACTIVE CORPUS LUTEUM

OVULATION

DEGENERATING CORPUS LUTEUM

RIPE FOLLICLE

GROWING FOLLICLE

IF NO PREGNANCY CORPUS LUTEUM DEGENERATES AND MENSTRUATION BEGINS

Fig. 12.4 The ovaries undergo cyclic changes each month. Ovulation occurs around the 14th day of the cycle. The ruptured follicle is then transformed into the corpus luteum, which degenerates around the 28th day. If pregnancy occurs, the corpus luteum persists and the cycles are interrupted.

This process, the discharge of detached endometrium and blood, is called **menstruation.** On the average, it takes three to five days for completion, but there is a great deal of individual variation. The "cramps" sometimes felt during menstruation are caused by contractions of the muscular walls of the uterus. After menstruation the uterus is ready to begin a new cycle, in preparation for the next ovulation.

How the Ovarian and Uterine Cycles Work Together

Changes taking place in the uterus are coordinated with changes taking place in the ovaries. This must be so in order for pregnancy to proceed. The fertilized egg must find a well developed endometrium when it enters the uterus. We have already indicated that the time of menstruation corresponds with the time when the corpus luteum degenerates, and that ovulation takes place about 14 days earlier. These relationships are shown in Fig. 12.4. Ovulation occurs when the endometrium is just about midway in its development. Since it takes a few days for the fertilized egg to reach the uterus, the egg enters the uterus when the endometrium is just approaching its peak of development.

This synchronization of ovarian and uterine cycles is not just a matter of chance. If a piece of the uterus is transplanted to another part of the body, it continues normal development and menstruation, despite the fact that all of the nerves to the transplanted tissue have been severed. This suggests that the menstrual cycle is under hormonal control. Further experiments show that hormones controlling the menstrual cycle come from the ovaries!

Fig. 12.5 Cyclic changes also take place in the uterus, shown here in cross section. The cycle begins with a poorly developed endometrium (top photo) which thickens (bottom photo), softens, and becomes enriched with blood vessels and glands.

Courtesy Dr. Hisaw, Howard University

Courtesy Dr. Hisaw, Howard University

151

1   BEFORE OVULATION

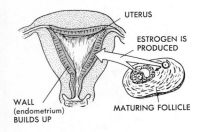

UTERUS

ESTROGEN IS
PRODUCED

WALL
(endometrium)
BUILDS UP

MATURING FOLLICLE

2   AFTER OVULATION

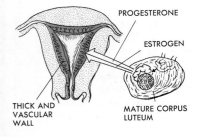

PROGESTERONE

ESTROGEN

THICK AND
VASCULAR
WALL

MATURE CORPUS
LUTEUM

3   DURING MENSTRUATION

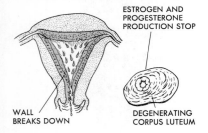

ESTROGEN AND
PROGESTERONE
PRODUCTION STOP

WALL
BREAKS DOWN

DEGENERATING
CORPUS LUTEUM

Fig. 12.6 The uterine cycles
depend on the cyclic secretion
of estrogen and progesterone
by the ovaries.

When the ovaries are removed, the endometrium does not develop, and menstruation never occurs. But if extracts of the follicle and corpus luteum are injected into the blood, the endometrium begins to thicken and develop as it normally does. Finally, the endometrium remains in the thick developed state as long as the extracts are administered, but when this treatment is stopped, menstruation occurs and the endometrium remains dormant until it receives more extract. Recall that normal menstruation begins when the corpus luteum begins to degenerate.

The ovaries secrete two types of hormone that control the uterine cycle. Cells of the follicle and the corpus luteum both secrete hormones called **estrogens.** These hormones stimulate growth in the endometrium. The estrogens are a general female sex hormone. They are necessary for the development of the female sex organs and breasts, for the distribution of fat and hair on the body, and for general body growth during adolescence. The other important ovarian hormone, secreted primarily by the corpus luteum is called **progesterone.** This hormone is sometimes called the hormone of pregnancy. Along with estrogen it induces a thickening of the endometrium, it stimulates the development of glands in the endometrium and in the breasts, and it *inhibits* contraction of the muscular walls of the uterus. Here, then (Fig. 12.6), is the sequence of steps in the uterine cycles. 1. Estrogen is secreted by the developing follicle and initiates growth of the endometrium. By the time ovulation occurs the endometrium is well on its way toward full development. 2. The corpus luteum now secretes a combination of estrogen and progesterone. This completes endometrial development. 3. When the corpus luteum degenerates, the source of progesterone, and a good deal of estrogens, is withdrawn. The thick endometrium can no longer be maintained and menstruation begins. Although this explains the coordination of ovarian and uterine cycles, it poses further questions. For instance, what controls the development of the follicles and corpus luteum?

Gonadotropic Hormones

The activities of the ovary (follicle and corpus luteum) are controlled by gonadotropic hormones secreted by the anterior pituitary gland. One of them—called **follicle stimulating hormone** (**FSH**)—stimulates the maturation process in the follicles. However, FSH by itself does not induce ovulation. A second hormone of the pituitary—called **luteinising hormone** (**LH**)—is required. This hormone, in combination with FSH, stimulates secretion of estrogens by the follicle and brings the follicle to the stage at which ovulation occurs. In addition LH is required for the development of the corpus luteum and the secretion of progesterone. A third pituitary hormone—called **luteotropic hormone** (**LTH**)—may also be necessary in some species for the secretion of progesterone. We see that the gonadotropic hormones have two roles: 1. they maintain the production of gametes (sperm and ova), and 2. they stimulate the secretion of sex hormones.

Secretion of the gonadotropic hormones are, in turn, influenced by the central nervous system and by sex hormones. The inter-relations between the central nervous system, the gonadotropins, and the sex hormones are complex. Although there has been much speculation, the precise details of these interactions, and the basis for the rhythmic activity, have not been completely worked out. One of the difficulties in filling in the details arises from our lack of a good method for measuring gonadotropic hormones in the blood. Another difficulty arises when we try to work out the role of the central nervous system. Also, because the nature of the ovulation cycle varies from species to species, experiments performed on one animal do not necessarily apply to another. Rabbits, for example, ovulate each time they mate.

WHEN THE UTERINE CYCLES STOP

Menopause: The menstrual cycle can be interrupted in either of two ways—by menopause or by pregnancy. When a woman reaches the age of 45 to 55 years the uterine cycles begin to change. At first they become irregular, then after a few months to a few years the cycles cease. During this time FSH is still produced but the ovaries do not respond; estrogen is no longer produced and ovulation ceases. During this period the woman must adjust both physiologically and psychologically to the withdrawal of estrogens.

Pregnancy: The uterine cycles are also stopped by pregnancy, which begins with fertilization of the ovum. At the climax of the sex act male sperm are deposited in the upper region of the vagina. From here some of the sperm may be transported through the uterus and into the oviducts, or fallopian tubes (see Fig. 12.7). The sperm are carried into the oviducts by their own swimming action and perhaps by movements of the uterus and oviducts. The sperm can probably remain in a healthy, fertile state for as long as 24 hours. The ovum probably remains fertilizable for a shorter time, perhaps for

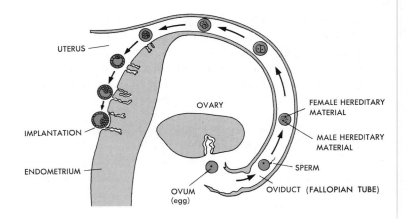

only a few hours. These two periods must overlap if fertilization is to take place.

Although millions of sperm are liberated by each ejaculation (release of male sperm), only one sperm out of the millions enters and fertilizes the ovum. Once the sperm enters the ovum (Fig. 12.7), its head expands and the hereditary material which it contains combines with the hereditary material of the ovum. Next, the egg begins to divide into a two-cell stage, then into a four-cell stage, eight, and so on. The process continues and forms a small ball of cells. By this time the developing mass of cells has moved through the oviduct and entered the uterus.

Cellular Specialization—Differentiation

The fertilized cell contains all of the information required to form a human being. When it divides it results in two cells which are exact replicas of one another. If these cells should happen to separate, not one but two human beings would result. Identical twins would be born. Apparently both cells in the two-cell stage are just alike. Nevertheless, we know that in the fully developed human being the cells are very different. Muscle cells differ from nerve cells which differ from liver cells. It follows that at some stage the cells in the developing embryo must begin to specialize. This process of specialization is called **differentiation.** The mechanism of how differentiation takes place is one of the great unsolved problems in biology. In attacking this problem two opposing ideas have been proposed. One idea is that at some stage of development, all cells do not receive the same genes. Thus the genes present in a cell which develops into a muscle cell are different from those in cells which become kidney cells. The alternative idea suggests that all cells in the body have the same genes, but that all of the genes are not active. A muscle cell, for example, would have the same set of genes as a kidney cell, but a different set of genes has been activated in the muscle cell. Today most scientists consider the second alternative as the better guess.

Implantation and the Placenta

Once the developing mass of cells has reached the uterus, it generally takes four or five days more before it firmly implants or attaches itself to the lining of the uterus. It begins this process by digesting away some of the endometrium. At this stage the embryo gets its nutrition from the endometrium. When implantation is complete the cells of the embryo and the endometrium form an important structure called the **placenta.** This structure enables the mother and embryo to exchange materials throughout the rest of the pregnancy period. It is through the placenta that the embryo sustains its parasitic life in the uterus, getting nutrients from the mother's body and depositing waste products to be expelled by the mother's kidney and lungs. The structure of the placenta is illustrated in Fig. 12.8. It consists of loops of blood capillaries supplied by and connected to the embryo through the **umbilical cord.** These capillary loops are bathed in tiny pools of blood supplied by the mother. The blood of the developing embryo and the mother are separated by thin membranes and do not mix. The exchange of nutrients and waste products takes place primarily by diffusion through these membranes.

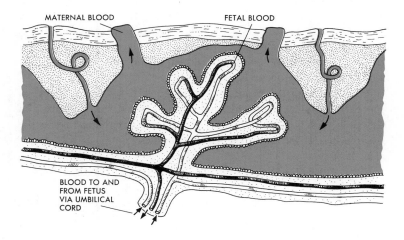

MATERNAL BLOOD   FETAL BLOOD

BLOOD TO AND FROM FETUS VIA UMBILICAL CORD

Fig. 12.8 The placenta is an organ of exchange between mother and fetus. An exchange of materials takes place through the loops of blood capillaries, which carry fetal blood and lie in close proximity to small "pools" of maternal blood. The maternal and fetal blood do not mix.

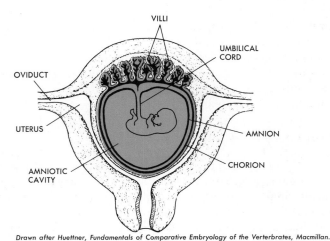

Drawn after Huettner, Fundamentals of Comparative Embryology of the Verterbrates, Macmillan.

Fig. 12.9 The fetus develops within a pool of fluid contained within the amnion.

The developing embryo forms two enveloping coats, the outer is called the **chorion,** and the inner, the **amnion** (Fig. 12.9). The amnion encloses the embryo within a pool of fluid. The chorion invades the endometrium with finger-like projections called **villi,** forming the embryo's contribution to the placenta.

Placenta Hormones

The placenta, in addition to performing the important function of an organ of exchange between mother and fetus, is also an important source of hormones. It secretes estrogens and progesterone; and in the early months of pregnancy it secretes a hormone called **chorionic gonadotropin.** This hormone is responsible for maintaining the corpus luteum before the placenta is capable of producing estrogens and progesterone. Thus, the corpus luteum persists during the early months of pregnancy, secreting estrogens and progesterone which maintain the endometrium. Progesterone also inhibits muscular contractions in the uterine wall. As a result, the menstruation that would ordinarily occur is prevented.

Chorionic gonadotropin which is secreted by the placenta in the early months of pregnancy is also excreted into the urine of the pregnant woman. This is the basis of pregnancy tests; the urine is tested for the presence of gonadotropins.

Birth and the Challenge of the New Environment

About 280 days after fertilization birth takes place. For some unknown reason, just before birth the proges-

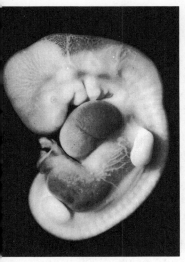

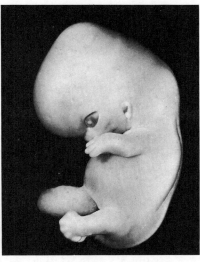

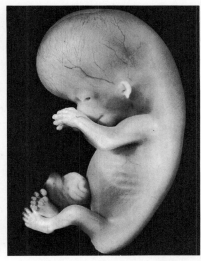

Fig. 12.10 The human embryo in successive stages of development. (A) shows the embryo at about the fourth week. The heart is very prominent in this photo; it is located just adjacent to the primitive arms. (B) shows the embryo in the sixth week. The limbs and the eyes and ears can be easily recognized. (C) shows the embryo after eight weeks of development, while (D) shows the infant lying within fetal membranes just prior to birth.

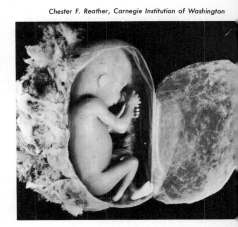

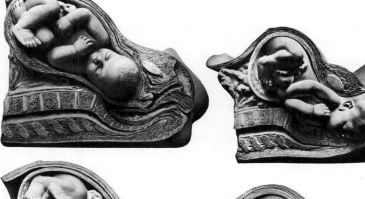

Fig. 12.11 These figures show the infant propelled through the birth canal at birth.

terone and estrogen hormone levels suddenly drop and the birth process begins with uterine contractions which become more and more regularly spaced. The uterine contractions give rise to the pains commonly called labor pains. In the first stage of birth, the fetus is pushed toward the opening of the uterus (the cervix), which begins to dilate. The membranes surrounding the fetus burst and release fluid. In the next stage the fetus is expelled, but it is still connected to the mother by the umbilical cord. The cord must then be cut. Finally, the placenta (the after-birth) is expelled. Figures 12.10 and 12.11 show some of the stages in the development and birth of a human being.

The new baby is no longer protected by its mother's body. It must breathe its own air, digest and absorb its own food, regulate its own temperature, salt and water content, and must ward off foreign invaders if it is to survive. Having lost access to the mother's internal environment, the infant must now begin to rely on its own homeostatic devices.

SUMMARY

Survival of the species depends on the ability of individuals to reproduce. Sexual reproduction takes place when a female gamete (ovum) is fertilized by a male gamete (sperm cell). The production of gametes and sex hormones by the ovaries (female) and testes (male) is controlled by **gonadotropic hormones** of the anterior pituitary. These hormones in turn are regulated by the nervous system and by sex hormones.

The normal production of sperm takes place in the seminiferous tubules of the testes and depends on the presence of the male hormone **testosterone** and on gonadotropic secretions from the anterior pituitary. During and following puberty, testosterone is secreted in significant amounts by interstitial cells of the testes. In addition to its effect on sperm production, testosterone promotes skeletal and muscular growth and the development of secondary sex characteristics. The supply of testosterone is controlled by anterior pituitary gonadotropic secretions.

The ovaries, which produce ova and sex hormones, and the uterus go through cyclic variations each month. About 14 days (on the average) following the onset of **menstruation,** an ovarian follicle ruptures and liberates a mature ovum. The ovum passes through the fallopian tubes to the uterus, where it finds a rapidly developing endometrium. The ruptured follicle becomes the secretory corpus luteum. If fertilization has not occurred, the corpus luteum degenerates and the thickened portions of the endometrium detach (about 14 days following ovulation), resulting in menstruation.

The development of the endometrium depends on the ovarian hormones, **estrogens** and **progesterone,** which provide a link between ovarian and uterine activities. Estrogens are also a general female sex hormone and are necessary for the development of feminine characteristics. The secretion of both estrogen and progesterone are controlled by gonadotropic hormones of the anterior pituitary. Gonadotropic hormones, in turn, are controlled by the nervous system and are subject to some feedback regulation by sex hormones.

Menstrual cycles stop during menopause and pregnancy. Fertilization probably takes place in the oviducts (fallopian tubes) when one of the millions of sperm, deposited in the vagina at the climax of the sex act, penetrates the ovum. The fertilized ovum divides several times during its migration to the uterus, where it becomes implanted in the endometrium and the **placenta** begins to develop. The placenta, which is connected to the embryo through the umbilical cord, performs two functions: 1. it is an *organ of exchange* between mother and embryo; 2. it first secretes *chorionic gonadotropin,* which maintains a secretory corpus luteum, and later it secretes estrogens and progesterone, which maintain the endometrium. Birth takes place about 280 days following fertilization.

FOR THOUGHT AND DISCUSSION

1 During the later months of pregnancy (beyond the first three months) the ovaries may be removed without ending pregnancy. However, during the early months the ovaries must remain intact if pregnancy is to continue. Can you suggest an explanation?

2 The hormone *oxytocin* is secreted by the posterior pituitary gland. Oxytocin stimulates contraction of the pregnant uterus. Mechanical stimulation of the cervix (opening of the uterus) and of the birth canal are believed to cause a reflex secretion of oxytocin. Do these facts suggest that a positive feedback loop may operate during childbirth? (Draw the loop.) How would this help the process of childbirth?

3 On very rare occasions an ovum is fertilized in the abdominal cavity and never enters the fallopian tube or uterus. To what extent do you think such a fertilized ovum would develop?

4 Some animals, such as human beings, ovulate periodically. Other animals, such as rabbits, cats, and raccoons, ovulate only after they have mated. Discuss the relative advantages and disadvantages of these two types of ovulation for the survival of the species.

SELECTED READINGS

Allen, R. D. "The Moment of Fertilization," *Scientific American* (July 1959).

Carlson, A. J., V. Johnson, and H. M. Cavert. *The Machinery of the Body,* 5th Ed. Chicago: University of Chicago Press, 1961.

Csapo, A. "Progesterone," *Scientific American* (April 1958) (reprint #163).

Guyton, A. C. *Textbook of Medical Physiology,* 3rd Ed. Philadelphia: W. B. Saunders Co., 1966.

Moog, F. "Up from the Embryo," *Scientific American* (February 1950).

Sussman, M. *Growth and Development,* 2nd Ed. Englewood Cliffs, New Jersey: Prentice-Hall, Inc., 1964.

Tepperman, J. *Metabolic and Endocrine Physiology.* Chicago: Yearbook Medical Publishers, Inc., 1963.

Winton, F. R. and L. E. Bayliss. *Human Physiology,* 5th Ed. Boston: Little, Brown, and Co., 1962.

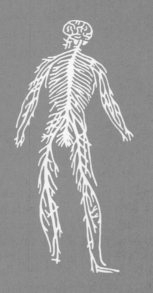

INDEX

162